# Radio Propagation – Principles and Practice

**Ian Poole, G3YWX**

Radio Society of Great Britain

Published by the Radio Society of Great Britain, Cranborne Road, Potters Bar, Herts EN6 3JE.

First published 2004

Reprinted 2005 & 2007

ISBN 9781 872309 97 2

*Publisher's note*

The opinions expressed in this book are those of the author and not necessarily those of the RSGB. While the information presented is believed to be correct, the author, the publisher and their agents cannot accept responsibility for consequences arising from any inaccuracies or omissions.

Cover photographs were kindly supplied by the Large Angle and Spectrometric Coronagraph experiment (LASCO), the Solar and Heliospheric Observatory (SOHO), Polar VIS (University of Iowa) and Jan Curtis.

Cover design: Laura Gleeson.
Production: Mark Allgar, M1MPA
Typography: Ray Eckersley
Illustrations: Bob Ryan

Printed in Great Britain by Latimer Trend & Company Ltd, Plymouth.

# Contents

Preface . . . . . . . . . . . . . . . . . . . . . . . . . . . . . . . . . . . . . . . . . . . . . . . . v

1  Electromagnetic waves  . . . . . . . . . . . . . . . . . . . . . . . . . . . . . . . . . 1

2  The atmosphere  . . . . . . . . . . . . . . . . . . . . . . . . . . . . . . . . . . . . . 13

3  The Sun . . . . . . . . . . . . . . . . . . . . . . . . . . . . . . . . . . . . . . . . . . . . 23

4  Propagation near the ground . . . . . . . . . . . . . . . . . . . . . . . . . . 35

5  Ionospheric propagation . . . . . . . . . . . . . . . . . . . . . . . . . . . . . . 37

6  Ionospheric disturbances, storms and auroras . . . . . . . . . . . 59

7  Predicting, assessing and using ionospheric propagation  67

8  Tropospheric propagation  . . . . . . . . . . . . . . . . . . . . . . . . . . . . 77

9  Meteor scatter . . . . . . . . . . . . . . . . . . . . . . . . . . . . . . . . . . . . . . 85

10  Space communications . . . . . . . . . . . . . . . . . . . . . . . . . . . . . . . 93

Index  . . . . . . . . . . . . . . . . . . . . . . . . . . . . . . . . . . . . . . . . . . . . 101

# Preface

**A** good knowledge of the way that signals propagate is essential for anyone associated with radio communication. This is particularly true for radio amateurs because an intimate knowledge of propagation and what each band can produce is a key to enabling the best to be made of the available equipment. Experienced operators know exactly when to be on the bands and also which band will be at its best at any particular time to contact the stations they want. Whether contacting stations on the other side of the globe on the HF bands, making contacts on the VLF bands, or operating at VHF, UHF or above, a good knowledge of the way signals propagate is essential. Understanding which enhancements or improvements there may be over the average or normal conditions and where and when to look for them can make the difference between just making run-of-the-mill contacts or filling the logbook with interesting and rare stations.

This knowledge is just as important to both radio amateurs and professionals, and was recognised by many of the early pioneers. Hertz, the man who is generally credited with knowingly transmitting the first electromagnetic signals, measured properties such as the velocity and explored elements such as reflection and refraction. Others like Marconi thought that it would be possible for signals to travel beyond the line of sight but with little knowledge about why this might be possible. Then in 1902 two scientists, Arthur Kennelly from the USA and Oliver Heaviside from the UK, suggested that there was an upper layer in the atmosphere where ionised gases existed and this enabled signals to be reflected. As a result of their researches, the layers in the ionosphere were for many years called the *Kennelly-Heaviside layers.*

Much research took place in the following years and an American named Lee de Forest suggested the reflecting layers in the upper atmosphere were at a height of approximately 62 miles. However it was not until 1924, when Edward (later Sir Edward) Appleton undertook some research, that the existence of the layer was confirmed. He initially discovered a layer at a height of 60 miles and later a higher layer between 150 and 200 miles above the Earth. He termed the different reflecting layers the *E and F layers.*

A couple of years later in 1926 scientists named Taylor and Hulbert from the US Naval Research Laboratory outlined the changing properties of the reflecting layers, mentioning that they changed over the course of a day and also with the changing seasons. They also described the idea of a skip distance.

Around this time one of the most prominent scientists involved in this area was Sidney Chapman. In 1931 he published a paper in which he set out the fundamental basis for our understanding today of the ionosphere.

Appleton made further contributions, publishing a complete theory of radio propagation in 1932. This contained an analysis of the Kennelly-Heaviside layer, and in the work he coined the term *ionosphere* to describe the areas of the atmosphere where ionisation was present and upon which sky-wave propagation depended.

Since then a great amount of work has been undertaken. One of the major elements in improving our knowledge of the ionosphere occurred when the first rockets were able to pass through it and collect data. This research considerably improved the scientific community's knowledge of many aspects of the ionosphere and particularly its composition at different times. Until this time it had not been possible to directly collect data as no probes existed that could travel this high.

The ionosphere particularly affects signals below about 30MHz. However, much work has also been undertaken to discover how signals travel at other frequencies above this, especially as technology developed and people could utilise these frequencies. Nowadays frequencies of many tens of gigahertz are commonly used and the modes of propagation are well understood.

Much research is still being undertaken into radio propagation at all frequencies. Many of the phenomena that affect radio signals are complicated and there is still much to learn. However, propagation can be a very rewarding study for the radio amateur. Not only will it enable the best use to be made of the available equipment and bands but it can also be very interesting.

The aim of this book has been to set out the basics in an easy-to-understand fashion as a guide and introduction. Obviously it is not possible to place everything into a volume of this size, but hopefully it will provide sufficient for many to gain more enjoyment from the hobby and for others it will provide a sufficient grounding on which to base further studies.

*Ian Poole*
*March 2004*

# CHAPTER 1

# Electromagnetic waves

R adio waves or signals are a form of *electromagnetic wave.* Accordingly, an understanding of the nature of such waves is a key element in being able to discover how radio waves propagate. As they travel, the radio waves are affected in different ways. Even moving through free space they decrease in amplitude as the signal spreads out. If they travel though the Earth's atmosphere they can be affected by it in a way which is governed by the nature of the waves and how they interact with their surroundings.

All electromagnetic waves consist of two elements: an electric and a magnetic component and these are inextricably linked. However, before examining the combined electromagnetic wave it is worth taking a look at electric and magnetic fields.

## Electric fields

An electric field is associated with *electric charges.* Any electrically charged object, whether it has a static charge associated with it or whether it is has an electric potential and is carrying a current, will have an electric field associated with it.

There are a number of properties associated with charges. It is commonly known that like charges repel one another and opposite charges attract. This can be demonstrated in various ways and it can often be seen in everyday life. For example, hair often stands on end after it has been brushed or combed because the hairs have the same charge on them and tend to repel one another. Examples like these are quite fun to demonstrate and occur because the voltages that are involved are very high and may typically rise to values of many kilovolts. However, even the comparatively low voltages that are found in electronic circuits exhibit the same effects, although to a much smaller degree.

Any object that has a charge, whether static or dynamic, will have an associated potential and an associated electric field. The electric field radiates out from the object with an electric potential as shown in Fig 1.1, falling away as the distance from it is increased. Take the example of a charged sphere with a potential of 10V. At the surface of the sphere the electrostatic

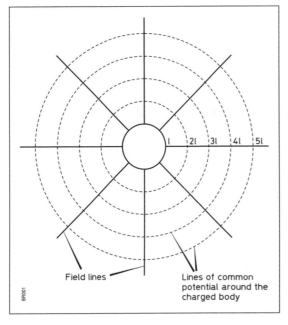

Field lines

Lines of common
potential around the
charged body

**Fig 1.1. Field lines and electric potential lines around a charged sphere**

potential is 10V but, as the distance from the sphere is increased, this potential starts to fall. It can be seen that it is possible to draw lines of equal potential around the sphere.

The potential falls away as the distance is increased from the sphere, and it can be shown that it falls away as the inverse of the distance, eg doubling the distance halves the potential. The variation of potential with distance from the sphere is shown in Fig 1.2.

The electric field gives the direction and magnitude of the force on a charged object. The *field intensity* is the negative value of the slope in Fig 1.2. This means that the steeper the slope, the greater the field intensity, and the negative value results from the fact that the slope is falling on the graph. The slope of a curve plotted on a graph is the rate of change of a variable. In this case it represents the rate of change of the potential with distance at a particular point. This is known as the *potential gradient*, and varies as the inverse square of the distance. In other words, doubling the distance reduces the potential gradient by a factor of four.

## Magnetic fields

Like electric fields, *magnetic fields* are also important and it is possible to draw many similarities between them. As already mentioned, electric charges attract and repel one another and so do their magnetic equivalents. Analogous to the positive and negative charges, magnets have two types of pole, namely a *north pole* and a *south pole*. Like poles repel and dissimilar ones attract. In the case of magnets it is also found that the magnetic field strength falls away, reducing as the inverse square of the distance.

The first magnets to be discovered were permanent magnets. After dynamic electricity was discovered and came into use it was noticed that there was a magnetic field associated with the current. This was detected by the fact that a compass needle placed close to the conductor was deflected. The lines of force are in a particular direction around the wire as shown in Fig 1.3. An easy method of determining which way they go around the conductor is to use the *corkscrew rule*. Imagine a right-handed corkscrew being driven into a cork on the direction of the current flow. The lines of force will be in the direction of rotation of the corkscrew.

**Fig 1.2. Variation of potential with distance from the charged sphere**

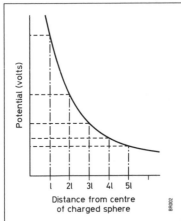

Potential (volts)

1    2l    3l    4l    5l

Distance from centre
of charged sphere

## Radio waves

As already mentioned, radio waves are a form of electromagnetic wave. They consist of the same type of radiation as light, ultra-violet, infra-red, etc, differing only in the wavelength or frequency of the radiation. The waves have both electric and magnetic components that are inseparable. The planes of the fields are at right-angles to each other and to the direction in which the wave is travelling. The wave can be visualised as shown in Fig 1.4.

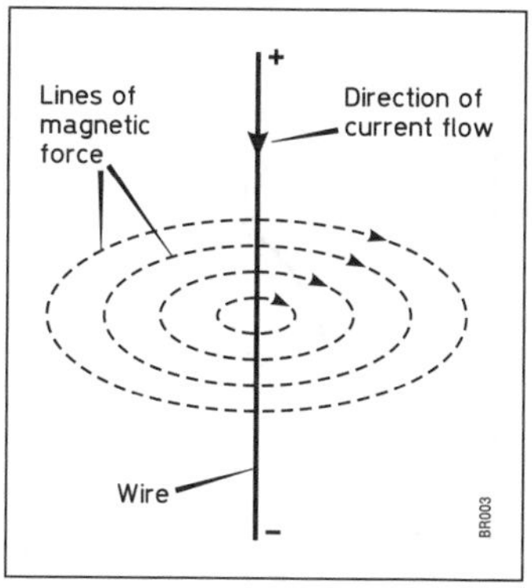

It is useful to see where the different elements of the wave emanate from. The electric component of the wave results from the voltage changes that occur as the antenna element is excited by the alternating waveform. The lines of force in the electric field run along the same axis as the antenna, but spreading out as they move away from it. This electric field is measured in terms of the change of potential over a given distance, eg volts per metre, and this is known as the *field strength*.

The other component, namely the magnetic field, is at right-angles to the electric field and hence it is at right-angles to the plane of the antenna. It is generated as a result of the current flow in the antenna.

**Fig 1.3. Lines of magnetic force around a current-carrying conductor**

## Wavelength, frequency and velocity

There are a number of basic properties of electromagnetic waves, or any repetitive waves for that matter, that are particularly important. The first is the *wavelength*, which is the distance between a given point on one cycle and the same point on the next cycle as shown in Fig 1.5. The easiest points to choose are the peaks as these are the simplest to locate. The wavelength was used in the early days of wireless to determine the position of a signal on the dial of a set. Although it is not used for this purpose today, it is nevertheless an important feature of any signal. The position of a signal on the dial of a radio set or its position within the radio spectrum is now determined by its frequency as this provides a more accurate and convenient method for determining the properties of the signal.

The second property of the electromagnetic wave is its *frequency*. This is the number of times a particular point on the wave moves up and down in a given time (normally a second). The unit of frequency is the *hertz* and it is equal to one cycle per second. This unit is named after the German scientist who discovered radio waves.

The frequencies used in radio are usually very high. Accordingly the prefixes 'kilo', 'mega', and 'giga' are often seen. 1kHz is a thousand hertz, 1MHz is a million hertz, and 1GHz is a thousand million hertz, ie 1000MHz. Originally the unit of frequency was not given a name and *cycles per second* (c/s) were used. Some older books may

**Fig 1.4. An electromagnetic wave**

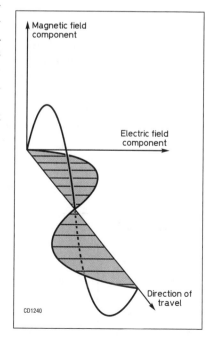

Magnetic field component

Electric field component

Direction of travel

CD1240

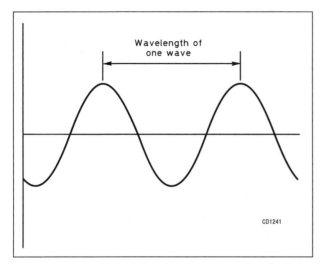

**Fig 1.5. The wave-length of an electro-magnetic wave**

show these units together with their prefixes ('kc/s', 'Mc/s' etc) for higher frequencies.

The third major property of the wave is its *speed*. Radio waves travel at the same speed as light. For most practical purposes this speed is taken to be 300 million metres per second although a more exact value is 299,792,500m/s.

## Frequency-to-wavelength conversion

The frequency and the wavelength are related to each other and it is very easy to determine the frequency of a signal if the wavelength is known, and vice versa if the frequency is known. The two are related to one another by the speed of the signal as shown:

$$\lambda = \frac{c}{f}$$

where $\lambda$ is the wavelength in metres, $f$ is the frequency in hertz and $c$ is the speed of radio waves (light), taken as 300,000,000m/s for all practical purposes.

As an example it can be seen that a signal with a wavelength of 300m has a frequency of 300,000,000/300 or one million hertz, ie 1MHz.

## Electromagnetic and radio spectrum

Electromagnetic waves have an enormous range, and as a result it is very convenient to see where each of the different forms of radiation fits within the spectrum as a whole. It can be seen that radio signals have the lowest frequency and hence the longest wavelengths. Above the radio spectrum other forms of radiation exist, including infra-red radiation, light, ultra-violet and a number of others as shown in Fig 1.6.

Even within the radio spectrum there is an enormous range of frequencies which extends over many decades. In order to be able to categorise the different areas and reduce these to more manageable sizes, the spectrum is divided into different segments as shown.

**Fig 1.6. Electromagnetic wave spectrum**

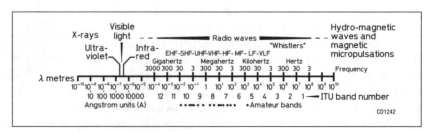

## Polarisation

Apart from the frequency, wavelength and speed of an electromagnetic wave, there are many other parameters it possesses that are of importance. One of these is its *polarisation*. In essence this defines the plane in which the wave is vibrating. As electromagnetic waves consist of an electric and a magnetic field vibrating at right-angles to each other it is necessary to adopt a convention to determine the polarisation of the signal. For this purpose the plane of the electric field is used.

The polarisation of a signal is important for a number of reasons. The first is that antennas are sensitive to polarisation. For most antennas it is easy to determine the polarisation because it is simply that of the plane of the elements in the antenna. In other words, an antenna with vertical elements will receive vertically polarised signals best, and an antenna with horizontal elements will receive horizontally polarised signals best.

Vertical and horizontal polarisations are the most straightforward and most commonly used forms and they fall into a category known as *linear polarisation*. However, this is not the only form as it is possible to generate waveforms that have *circular polarisation*.

Circular polarisation can be visualised by imagining a signal propagating from an antenna that is rotating. The tip of the electric field vector can be seen to trace out a helix or corkscrew as it travels away from the antenna. Circular polarisation can be either right- or left-handed, dependent upon the direction of rotation as seen from the transmitting antenna.

It is also possible to obtain *elliptical polarisation*. This occurs when there is a combination of both linear and circular polarisation. Again this can be visualised by imagining the tip of the electric field tracing out an elliptically shaped corkscrew.

The polarisation of a signal is very important. An antenna receiving a signal will produce the largest output when the incoming signal has the same polarisation as the antenna. This means that in free space both the transmitting and receiving antennas should have the same polarisation (ie be in the same plane) to produce the best signal at the receiving antenna. In theory, if the antennas are linearly polarised and are at right-angles to each other (ie *cross-polarised*) then the output from the receiving antenna should be zero. A similar situation exists for circular polarisation where cross-polarised antennas will produce no output. In other words, a left-handed antenna will not give an output when a right-handed circularly polarised signal appears.

However, it is possible for linearly polarised antennas to receive circularly polarised signals and vice versa. The strength will be equal whether the linearly polarised antenna is mounted vertically, horizontally or in any other plane but directed towards the arriving signal. There will be some degradation because the signal level will be 3dB less than if a circularly polarised antenna of the same sense was used. The same situation exists when a circularly polarised antenna receives a linearly polarised signal.

For terrestrial applications it is found that once a signal has been transmitted then its polarisation will remain broadly the same. However, reflections

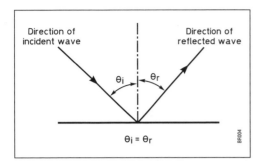

Fig 1.7. Reflection of an electromagnetic wave

from objects in the path can change the polarisation. As the received signal is the sum of the direct signal plus a number of reflected signals the overall polarisation of the signal can change slightly although it usually remains broadly the same. When reflections take place from the ionosphere, then greater changes may occur.

Different types of polarisation are used in different applications as appropriate. Linear polarisation is by far the most widely used. Vertical polarisation is often used for mobile or point-to-point applications. This is because many vertical antennas have an omni-directional radiation pattern and it means that the antennas do not have to be re-orientated as positions are changed if for example they are on a moving vehicle. For other applications the polarisation is often determined by antenna considerations. Some large multi-element antenna arrays can be mounted in a horizontal plane more easily than in the vertical plane. This is because the antenna elements are at right-angles to the vertical tower or pole on which they are mounted and therefore by using an antenna with horizontal elements there is less physical and electrical interference between the two. This determines the standard polarisation in many cases.

In some applications there are performance differences between horizontal and vertical polarisation. For example, medium-wave broadcast stations generally use vertical polarisation because ground-wave propagation over the Earth is considerably better using vertical polarisation, whereas horizontal polarisation shows a marginal improvement for long-distance communications using the ionosphere. Circular polarisation is sometimes used for satellite communications as there are some advantages in terms of propagation and in overcoming the fading caused if the satellite is changing its orientation.

## Refraction, reflection and diffraction

As radio signals travel they interact with objects and changes within the media in which they travel. As they do this the signals can undergo reflections, refraction and diffraction in the same way that occurs for light. There are some slight differences as a result of the different wavelengths but the same principles hold true in exactly the same way.

*Reflection* of light is an everyday occurrence. Mirrors are commonplace and can be seen in houses and many other places. Shop windows also provide another illustration for this phenomenon, as do many other areas. Radio waves are similarly reflected by many surfaces.

When reflection occurs, it can be seen that the angle of incidence is equal to the angle of reflection for a conducting surface as would be expected for light (Fig 1.7), and there is normally some loss, either through absorption or as a result of some of the signal passing into the medium.

For radio signals surfaces such as the sea provide very good reflecting surfaces. Desert areas are poor reflectors and other types of land fall in between these two extremes. In general, though, wet areas provide better reflectors.

It is also possible for radio waves to be *refracted*. The concept of light waves being refracted is very familiar, especially as it can be easily demonstrated by placing a part of a stick or pole in water and leaving the remaining section in air. It is possible to see the apparent change or bend as the stick enters the water. Mirages also demonstrate refraction and a very similar phenomenon can be noticed on hot days when a shimmering effect can be seen when looking along a straight road. Radio waves are affected in the same way (Fig 1.8).

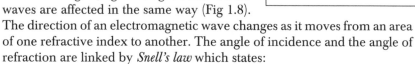

**Fig 1.8. Refraction of an electromagnetic wave at the boundary between two areas of differing refractive index**

The direction of an electromagnetic wave changes as it moves from an area of one refractive index to another. The angle of incidence and the angle of refraction are linked by *Snell's law* which states:

$$n_1 \sin \theta_1 = n_2 \sin \theta_2$$

For radio signals there are comparatively few instances where the signals move abruptly from a region with one refractive index to a region with another. It is far more common for there to be a comparatively gradual change. This causes the direction of the signal to bend rather than undergo an immediate change in direction.

Radio signals may also undergo *diffraction*. When signals encounter an obstacle they tend to travel around them as shown in Fig 1.9, and this can mean that a signal may be received from a transmitter even though it may be 'shaded' by a large object between them. To understand how this happens it is necessary to look at *Huygen's principle*. This states that each point on a spherical wavefront can be considered as a source of a secondary wavefront. Even though there will be a shadow zone immediately behind the obstacle, the signal will diffract around the obstacle and start to fill the void. Diffraction is more pronounced when the obstacle becomes sharper and more like a 'knife edge'. For a radio signal a mountain ridge may provide a sufficiently

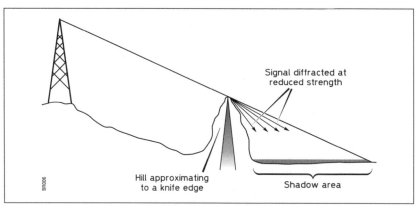

**Fig 1.9. Diffraction of a radio signal around an obstacle**

sharp edge, while a more rounded hill will not produce such a marked effect. Low-frequency signals diffract more markedly than higher-frequency ones, and it is for this reason that signals on the long-wave band are able to provide coverage even in hilly or mountainous terrain where signals at VHF and higher would not.

## Doppler shift

Doppler shifts occur on sound waves and the same is true for electromagnetic waves, and in particular radio waves. The original effect was established by Doppler in 1842 and relates to frequency changes caused when transmitters or receivers move.

The traditional example is that of a steam train blowing its whistle while passing by. As the train comes towards the listener the whistle appears to be high in frequency, falling as it passes the listener and moves away. It occurs because when the train is moving towards the listener the waves are compressed and the apparent frequency is increased. Then, as the train moves away, the sound signals are expanded, resulting in a decrease in the apparent frequency.

The same effect occurs with radio waves, often being observed when the reflective medium is moved. When this occurs the signal waves are compressed or expanded in exactly the same way, resulting in a perceived change in frequency.

## Signals in free space

In the simplest scenario, radio signals may be considered to travel outwards from the point where they are radiated by an antenna. A rather useful two-dimensional analogy is that of a stone being dropped into water and the resulting circular ripples that move away from the source. As they move outwards they reduce in level, and finally disappear to the eye. In the case of radio signals they spread out in all directions as if on the surface of a sphere and reduce in strength because the area of the sphere is increasing as they travel further away from the source. This form of propagation is called *free space propagation* because there are no external influences on the signal.

The signal reduces in strength and it can be shown that it falls in proportion to the radius squared, and hence the signal strength is inversely proportional to the distance squared from the transmitter to the receiver. This is written mathematically as $1/d^2$, where $d$ is the distance from the transmitter. This means that at a distance 2m from the transmitter, the signal strength is equal to a quarter of the strength that it is at 1m distance; and at 100m, it is only one-ten thousandth of the strength.

Sometimes terrestrial signal paths may approximate to free space transmissions, especially over short distances. This may be the case for short-range 'walkie-talkies' or items such as mobile phones that would not use communications over long distances. However, even these are subject to greater levels of attenuation than would be suggested by the basic calculations because the signals are absorbed by vegetation, buildings or other objects that may fall within the transmission path.

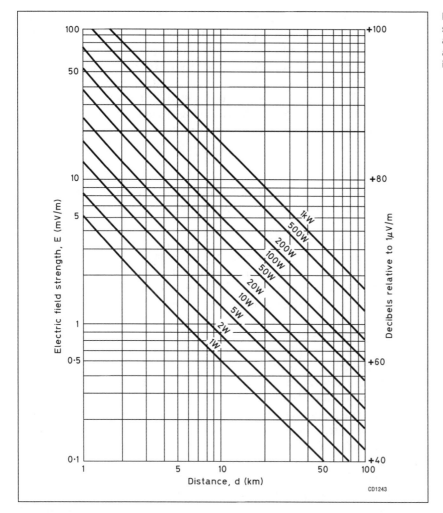

**Fig 1.10.** Field strength levels from an omni-directional antenna radiating into free space

## Field strength

Measurements or calculations of the strength of an electromagnetic wave sometimes need to be made. The intensity of a radio wave at any point in space may be expressed in terms of the strength of its electric field. This is expressed in terms of the electric force between points spaced one metre apart, ie volts per metre.

As an electromagnetic wave travels away from the antenna it spreads out over an increasing area. Under free space conditions it is easy to calculate what the signal strength will be because the signal follows an inverse square-law relationship. In other words, if the distance doubles the signal decays by a factor of two squared or four.

Fig 1.10 shows the calculated field strength levels when a transmitter radiates a signal into free space. If the antenna has a gain then this can be easily transferred onto the graph to give the correct levels.

Signals encountered by radio amateurs and listeners will not completely follow the free space calculations because of the Earth itself as well as other objects in or close to the signal path. Conditions in the atmosphere, in particular the troposphere and the ionosphere, also have a significant effect. This makes it more difficult to predict the signal strength at a given point.

Calculating the field strength of a signal is normally of little use on its own. It is the actual signal voltage at the input of the receiver that is needed. Assuming that the antenna for the receiving system is a half-wave dipole then the voltage input can be calculated from:

$$V = \frac{48.7 \times E}{f}$$

where $V$ is the voltage at the input of the receiver in microvolts, $E$ is the field strength at the antenna in microvolts per metre and $f$ is the frequency of operation.

If another type of antenna is used, then its gain or loss can be used to modify the answer. In other words, if the antenna has a gain of 6dB over a dipole this represents a voltage increase by a factor of two and the answer can be adjusted accordingly. With knowledge of the performance of the radio receiver it is possible to determine whether the signal will be sufficiently strong to copy.

## Path loss

In many calculations it is necessary to determine the loss in a given path. Whilst it is not always easy to accurately determine the loss via an ionospheric path because of the great number of variables, paths in free space can be calculated quite accurately. It is common to calculate the path loss to and from a satellite. With the enormous distances to satellites in geostationary orbit (at altitudes of 35,860km above the equator) losses caused purely by the distances involved are very large. By having a knowledge of the path loss, it is possible to optimise the requirements for receiver sensitivity, antenna gains and transmitter power. These are particularly important because increasing the transmitter power or the antenna size at the satellite can be very costly.

The loss can be calculated from the formula:

$$\text{Loss (dB)} = 32.45 + 20 \log_{10} f + 20 \log_{10} d$$

where $f$ is the frequency in megahertz and $d$ is the path distance in kilometres.

Notice that the loss increases with frequency. Fortunately antenna gains can be increased more easily at higher frequencies as antenna sizes are smaller, and this can be used to compensate this effect.

This means that if someone was directly below a satellite in geostationary orbit then the signal loss to the satellite at a frequency of 10GHz would be:

$$= 32.45 + 20 \log_{10} (10000) + 20 \log_{10} (35860)$$
$$= 32.45 + 20 \times 4 + 20 \times 4.55$$
$$= 203.45 \text{dB}$$

In view of this enormous loss geostationary satellite systems need to be carefully designed to ensure that a sufficiently good signal can be received.

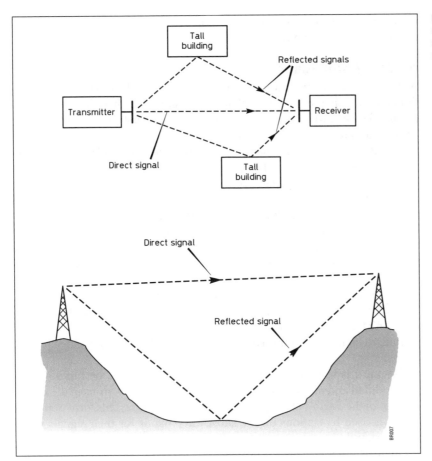

**Fig 1.11. Signals arrive at a receiver via several different paths**

Systems using satellites in a lower orbit are not nearly as critical because path losses can be very much lower.

## Multi-path signals

Very few terrestrial signals that are sent and received travel over a simple single straight path. Instead signals usually arrive at the receiver over a variety of paths and the overall received signal is the sum of several signals. This situation arises because they travel out in a variety of directions and are reflected by objects including buildings, hills, and other objects as shown in Fig 1.11. Even the Earth reflects the signal.

Often this type of scenario is referred to as *multi-path propagation*, and it gives rise to phenomena such as the deep fading and distortion that sometimes arises on broadcast FM signals. As the path length for each of these signals is slightly different, it means that they take a different time to arrive at the receiver and will arrive with a different phase. Accordingly they sometimes add together, while at other times they subtract. It is for this reason that VHF and UHF hand-held transceivers only need to move a few centimetres for signal strengths to vary very considerably. As wavelengths are

**11**

comparatively short, path differences do not have to be that large for signals to arrive in antiphase.

## Modes of propagation

Although many of the properties of radio signals which have been mentioned in this chapter relate to the idealised situation when the signal is not modified by external influences, this is not the case for most circumstances. The signals are affected in a number of ways, and this governs the way they travel. At some frequencies they may only travel over short distances whereas at others they may be heard over distances of many thousands of kilometres. The way in which signals propagate can be split into four main categories as detailed below.

The most obvious form of propagation is *free space* propagation. Here the radio signals travel in free space, or away from other objects which influence the way in which they travel. It is only the distance from the source which affects the way in which the field strength reduces. This type of propagation is encountered with signals travelling to and from satellites.

The second type is where signals travel via *ground-wave* propagation. When signals travel as a ground wave they are modified by the ground or terrain over which they travel. They also tend to follow the Earth's curvature. Signals heard on the medium-wave band during the day use this form of propagation.

The third type is called *ionospheric* propagation. Here the radio signals are modified and influenced by the action of the free electrons in the upper reaches of the Earth's atmosphere called the *ionosphere*. This form of propagation is used by stations on the short-wave bands for their signals to be heard around the globe.

Finally there is *tropospheric* propagation. Here the signals are influenced by the variations of refractive index in the troposphere just above the Earth's surface. Tropospheric propagation is often the means by which signals at VHF and above are heard over extended distances.

# CHAPTER 2

# The atmosphere

**T**he atmosphere is not only crucial in enabling life to be supported on Earth but it also has a major effect on radio signals. It can change their direction, enabling them to be heard over much greater distances than would otherwise be possible. It also has other effects such as introducing additional loss in some instances or possibly changing the polarisation.

The atmosphere is the gaseous envelope that surrounds the surface of the Earth, and is generally considered to extend to an altitude of around 9500km or 6000 miles. However, at its very outer reaches it is exceedingly thin and the density of the gas is extremely low. In fact the density of the air in the

**Fig 2.1. The Earth viewed from outer space** *(courtesy NASA)*

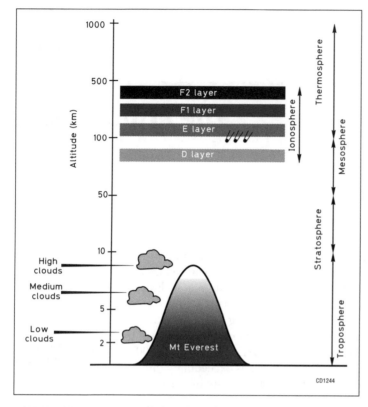

**Fig 2.2. The areas of the Earth's atmosphere**

atmosphere falls rapidly with altitude and accordingly the pressure also falls. At an altitude of only 6km it is half its sea-level value. The pressure continues to halve for approximately every 6km increase in altitude, and at an altitude of around 80km, just below the ionosphere, it is only 0.00001 of atmospheric pressure at sea level.

The atmosphere is made up from a variety of gases. Although the natural tendency would be for the denser gases to settle to the lower altitudes, leaving the lighter gases higher up, this does not occur in practice. The reason for this is that the atmospheric winds continually mix the gases and as a result the proportion of each gas remains virtually the same up to altitudes of 80 to 90km. The principal constituents in the atmosphere are nitrogen (78%) and oxygen (21%). The remaining gases form only about 1%. Of these argon (0.9%) has the highest level, followed by carbon dioxide (0.03%) and varying amounts of water vapour dependent upon the humidity level at that time. Other gases that are found include hydrogen, ozone, methane, carbon monoxide, and some of the inert elements including neon, krypton and xenon.

## Atmospheric layers

The atmosphere can be divided up in to a variety of layers according to the different properties they exhibit. Unfortunately there is no single set of nomenclature that can be employed because there are several different systems in use by different organisations and interests. The set that is most applicable for propagation studies is the meteorological one given in Fig 2.2. From this it can be seen that the main layers are the *troposphere* closest to the Earth. Above this is the *stratosphere*, followed by the *mesosphere*, and finally there is the *thermosphere*. The boundaries between these layers are based on the temperature variations that exist and as a result the exact altitudes of the different areas vary from day to day, and according to their location.

The temperature in the troposphere falls as the altitude increases. It falls to nearly –60°C, typically at an altitude of around 10km. It then rises in the stratosphere, almost reaching 0°C at the border with the mesosphere, where again the temperature falls to around −90°C at the border with the thermosphere. Then the temperature rises again, reaching around 1200°C.

There are two main areas of the atmosphere that affect radio signals. The first is the *troposphere*, and the second is the *ionosphere* which extends over the mesosphere and thermosphere. These two areas act on radio signals in very different ways but enable them to travel over distances that are greater than just the line of sight.

## The troposphere

This is the portion of the atmosphere that is closest to the ground and it is here that most of the conditions that affect the weather occur. Clouds may extend virtually from ground level to the highest ones which may reach as high as 8 or 10km. High- and low-pressure areas also exist, as do winds and the other features that govern the weather conditions.

Another feature of the troposphere that is of importance is that the pressure and temperature fall with increasing altitude. The temperature falls steadily to around −60°C at the *tropopause* – the point at which the temperature starts to rise and the boundary with the stratosphere.

The refractive index of the air in the troposphere plays a major role in radio signal propagation. This is dependent upon a number of factors including the temperature, the pressure and the level of humidity. There are noticeable changes in the values of all three of these measures close to the ground and as a result tropospheric propagation normally occurs at altitudes less than about 3km.

## The ionosphere

The ionosphere is an area of the atmosphere that is contained within more than one of the meteorological areas. Encompassed by the mesosphere and the thermosphere, it is an area that is characterised by the existence of positive ions (and more importantly for radio signals free electrons), and it is from the existence of the ions that it gains its name.

The number of free electrons starts to rise at altitudes of approximately 30km but it is not until around 80 or 90km are reached that the concentration is sufficiently high to start to have a noticeable effect on radio signals.

In essence the ionisation in the upper atmosphere is caused by radiation from the Sun. However, there are other aspects that need to be considered. In view of the very high temperatures and the low pressure, gases in the upper reaches of the atmosphere exist mainly in a monatomic form rather than molecules. At lower altitudes the gases are in the normal molecular form but, as the altitude increases, the monatomic forms are more in abundance, and at altitudes of around 150km most of the gases are in a monatomic form. This is very important because the monatomic forms of the gases are very much easier to ionise than the molecular ones.

The Sun emits vast quantities of radiation of all wavelengths and this travels towards the Earth, first reaching the outer areas of the atmosphere. Ionisation occurs when radiation of sufficient intensity strikes an atom or a

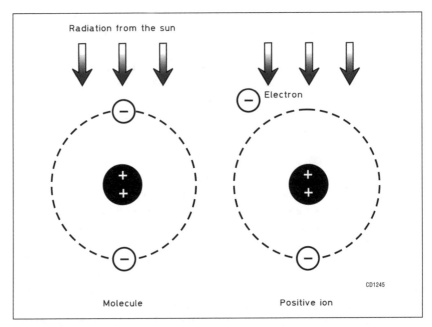

Radiation from the sun

Electron

Molecule

Positive ion

CD1245

molecule – energy may be absorbed from the radiation and an electron detached, producing a free electron and a positive ion. The simple example of a helium atom is given in Fig 2.3, although other gases including oxygen and nitrogen are far more common.

The radiation from the Sun appears as a variety of wavelengths but can be considered to be photons. From Fig 2.3 it can be seen that the electrons are orbiting the central nucleus which consists of protons and neutrons.

Electrons are tied or bound to their orbit around the nucleus by electrostatic forces. The electron is negatively charged and the nucleus is positively charged – since there are equal numbers of electrons and protons in any molecule it is electrostatically neutral. When a photon strikes the atom or molecule, the photon transfers its energy to the electron as excess kinetic energy. Under some circumstances this excess energy may exceed the binding energy in the atom or molecule and the electron escapes the influence of the positive charge of the nucleus. This leaves a positively charged nucleus or *ion* and a negatively charged electron, although as there are the same number of positive ions and negative electrons the whole gas still remains with an overall neutral charge.

Of the radiation that reaches the Earth, most of the ionisation is caused by ultra-violet light, although other wavelengths also play a part in the process. Each time an atom or molecule is ionised a small amount of energy is used. This means that as the radiation passes further into the atmosphere, its intensity reduces. It is for this reason that the ultra-violet radiation causes most of the ionisation in the upper reaches of the ionosphere, but at lower altitudes extreme ultra-violet and X-rays give rise to most of it. This reduction in these forms of radiation protects us on the surface of the Earth from their harmful effects.

Although the radiation is at its most intense at the edge of the atmosphere, the levels of ionisation vary with altitude. There are a number of reasons for this – the density of the gases varies and there is also a variation in the proportions of monatomic and molecular forms of the gases. These and a variety of other phenomena mean that there are variations in the level of ionisation with altitude.

Often the ionosphere is thought of as a number of distinct layers. This is a convenient way of picturing its structure but it is not strictly true. There is ionisation over the whole of the ionosphere, and its level varies at different altitudes, rising and falling. The peaks in level may be considered as the different layers or regions. These regions are given letter designations: *D*, *E* and *F* regions. There

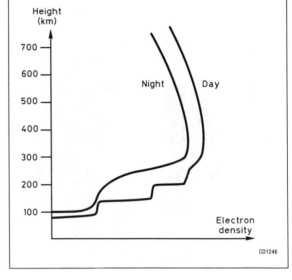

**Fig 2.4. The typical electron distribution in the ionosphere**

is in fact a *C region* beneath the others but the level of ionisation is very low and it does not affect radio signals. Accordingly it is rarely mentioned. It can be seen quite clearly from Fig 2.4 that the different regions are peaks in the levels of ionisation. This is only a very approximate guide as the levels vary considerably as the result of a number of other factors.

One of the main reasons for the variation of the electron density in the ionosphere changing with time is the fact that the radiation from the Sun is only present during the day. This radiation causes the atoms and molecules to split into free electrons and positive ions but the reverse effect also occurs. When a negative electron meets a positive ion, the fact that dissimilar charges attract means that they will be pulled towards one another and they may combine. This means that two opposite effects of splitting and recombination are taking place. This is known as a *state of dynamic equilibrium*. Accordingly the level of ionisation is dependent upon the rate of ionisation and recombination.

The effect can be likened to a tank of water being filled. If water is drawn off the level of the water in the tank is dependent upon the amount of water being run into it as well as the amount of water being drawn out. Here the water being used to fill the tank is equivalent to the radiation causing ionisation, and the water being drawn out is equivalent to the recombination. The depth of water in the tank is the amount of ionisation. If the Sun sets and the radiation is removed this is like the water supply flowing into the tank being stopped. This will result in the level of water in the tank falling.

## Ionospheric regions

The different regions in the ionosphere have many different characteristics in the way they are generated, are sustained and the way they affect radio waves. In view of this it is worth taking a closer look at each one in detail and

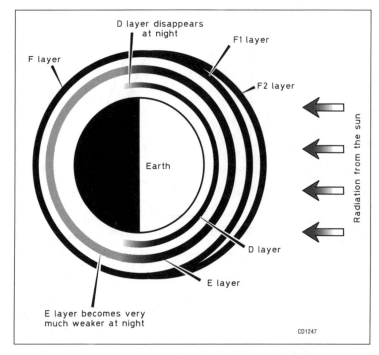

**Fig 2.5. A simplified view of the layers in the ionosphere over the period of a day**

the way they vary over the complete day during light and darkness (Fig 2.5).

The condition of the Sun also has a major effect on the state of the ionosphere. The level of radiation that it emits changes with time and this can have a significant effect on the ionosphere. These changes are investigated in the next chapter.

## D region

This region is the lowest one that significantly affects radio signals, existing at altitudes between about 60 and 90km. It is only present to any degree during the day when radiation from the Sun is present, levels of ionisation falling rapidly when the latter sets. It mainly has the affect of absorbing or attenuating radio signals, particularly in the LF and MF portions of the radio spectrum, its effect reducing with frequency. At night it has little effect on most radio signals, although there is still a sufficient level of ionisation for it to refract VLF signals.

The layer is chiefly generated by the action of a form of radiation known as *Lyman α radiation* which has a wavelength of 1215 ångstroms (1215Å) and ionises nitric oxide gas present in the atmosphere. Hard X-rays also contribute to the ionisation, especially towards the peak of the solar cycle.

## E region

The region that is found above the D region is obviously known as the *E region*. It exists at altitude between about 100 and 125km. Instead of attenuating signals this layer chiefly 'reflects' or, more correctly, *refracts* them, although they are still attenuated to some degree.

In this region, like the D region, the level of ionisation falls relatively quickly after dark as the electrons and ions re-combine and it virtually disappears at night. However, the residual night-time ionisation in the lower part of the E region causes some attenuation of signals in the lower portions of the HF part of the radio spectrum.

The ionisation in this region results from a number of types of radiation. Soft X-rays produce much of the ionisation, although extreme ultra-violet (EUV) rays (very-short-wavelength ultra-violet light) also contribute. Broadly the radiation that produces ionisation in this region has wavelengths between about 10 and 100Å. The degree to which all of the constituents contribute depends upon the state of the Sun and the latitude at which the observations are made.

## F region

The highest and most important region from the point of view of long-distance HF communications is the F region. During the daytime when radiation is being

**Table 2.1. Summary of forms of radiation causing ionisation in the ionosphere**

| Region | Primary ionising radiation forms |
|--------|----------------------------------|
| C | Cosmic rays |
| D | Lyman α, hard x-rays |
| E | Soft X-rays and some extreme ultra-violet |
| F1 | Extreme ultra-violet, some ultra-violet |
| F2 | Ultra-violet |

received from the Sun, it splits into two, the lower one being the F1 region and the higher one the F2 region. Of these the F1 region is more of an inflection point in the electron density curve and it generally only exists in the summer.

The altitude of the layers varies considerably and figures given should only be taken as a rough guide. Being the highest of the ionospheric regions, it is greatly affected by the state of the Sun as well as other factors including the time of day, the year and so forth. Typically the F1 layer is found at around an altitude of 300km with the F2 layer above it at around 400km. The combined F layer may then be centred around 250 to 300km.

The F layer acts as a 'reflector' of signals in the HF portion of the spectrum, enabling worldwide communications to be established. It is the main region associated with HF signal propagation.

Like the D and E layers the level of ionisation of this region varies over the course of the day, falling at night as the radiation from the Sun disappears. However, it remains much higher. The density of the gases is much lower, and as a result the recombination of the ions and electrons takes place more slowly, at about a quarter of the rate that it occurs in the E region. Consequently it still has an effect on signals at night, being able to return many to Earth, although it has a reduced effect in some aspects.

As the F region is at the highest altitude, it experiences the full force of the solar radiation, and much of the ionisation results from ultra-violet light in the middle of the spectrum as well as those portions of the spectrum with very short wavelengths. Typically the radiation that causes the ionisation is between the wavelengths of 100 and 1000Å, although extreme ultra-violet light is responsible for some ionisation in the lower areas of the F region. See Table 2.1.

## Ionospheric variations

It has already been seen that the time of day causes some very significant changes in the state of the ionosphere as the level of ionisation falls at night. However, there are many other factors that have an effect on the ionosphere. The main one is the Sun itself but this will be discussed in the next chapter. Other factors include the season and the position on the globe.

### Seasonal changes

In just the same way that the amount of heat places on the Earth receive varies with the seasons, so does the amount of radiation received by the ionosphere. This results from the fact that in summer the radiation spreads over a smaller area as the Earth's surface is closer to being at right-angles to the direction of the radiation. In winter, the surface is at a greater angle and the radiation has to spread over a larger area. Consequently the ionosphere receives less radiation in winter than summer.

The D and E regions respond as expected, with lower levels of ionisation in winter than summer, and the F1 region also follows a similar pattern. However, for the F2 region there are other influencing factors and it responds in a different way.

For the F2 region, the heating effect of the Sun plays a crucial role in the way it responds. The temperature during the winter is much less than in the summer as a result of the heat from the Sun being spread over a larger area because the Sun is lower in the sky. In summer the gas temperature rises in the F2 region so the activity in the air rises and a greater number of molecules rise higher up into the atmosphere. In winter, as the temperature falls, the heavier molecules fall, leaving the lighter atoms to rise to the top.

This means that in winter there is a higher proportion of atoms at the higher altitude of the F2 region. Atoms are easier to ionise than gas molecules, and so the number of suitable targets for the radiation to ionise also rises. As a result the levels of daytime ionisation are actually higher in winter than they are in the summer. The overall effect is that the peak daytime levels of ionisation rise higher in winter than summer, but they fall away to a lower level as the Sun's radiation is present for a smaller proportion of the time.

### Geographical variations

The levels of ionisation are also affected by the position on the globe. There are naturally variations arising from the latitude – polar regions receive less radiation and the equatorial regions enjoy much higher levels. Broadly this results in higher levels of ionisation for the D, E and F1 regions in equatorial areas than towards the poles.

The F2 region has a number of other factors that affect its level of ionisation, including the Earth's magnetic field and it also receives ionisation from other sources. As a result of these the levels of ionisation are higher around Asia and Australia than they are over the western hemisphere, including Africa, Europe, and North America.

## Beyond the ionosphere

The Earth's atmosphere reaches up to many hundreds of kilometres. It is generally accepted that the ionosphere extends out to altitudes of 600km. Here the density of the gases is so low that the levels of ionisation fall to a point where they have no noticeable affect on radio signals.

Beyond the ionosphere, there are still regions associated with the Earth that have an effect on radio signal propagation. The main area of importance is associated with the magnetic field that surrounds the Earth. This arises from the movement of the fluids within the core of the Earth and the resulting currents that flow. This gives rise to the magnetic north and south poles. See Fig 2.6.

Emanating from the Sun is a steady stream of charged particles in the form of the *solar wind*. As the particles are charged they interact with the Earth's geomagnetic field and a shock wave is set up. This is named the *magneto-sheath*, and the solar wind flows around this. It is at a distance of about 10 Earth radii from the Earth. The action of the solar wind distorts the Earth's magnetic or geomagnetic field, creating a long tail extending away from the Sun. Thus the magnetic field is compressed on the day side of the Earth, and drawn out on the night side. The geomagnetic field protects the Earth from the solar wind, which does not enter inside the area within the magnetosheath – this region is called the *magnetosphere*.

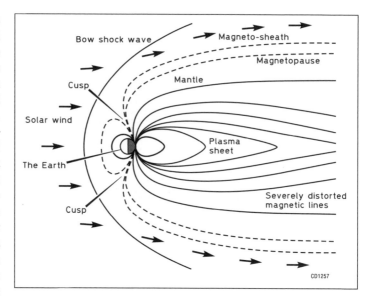

**Fig 2.6. Beyond the ionosphere**

Within the magnetosphere there are areas where charged particles from the solar wind become trapped by the geomagnetic lines of force. They travel at very large velocities and oscillate back and forth in what are named the *Van Allen belts* after their discoverer. Currently much is unknown about these belts and more work is needed before there is a complete understanding of the way the particles from the solar wind become trapped.

What is known is that during periods of high solar activity, when the solar wind greatly increases, it causes electrons trapped in the Van Allen belts in the magnetosphere to enter the Earth's atmosphere at both poles, creating the auroras, ie the Northern and Southern Lights. These can only be seen towards the poles but they are dramatic and quite beautiful, appearing as slowly changing lights in the sky.

# 3

# The Sun

T he Sun is the central point of the Solar System. It is the sole provider of energy that enables life on Earth to exist, and it is also the source of radiation that gives rise to the ionosphere. Upon it depends the state of the ionosphere and hence it is of great interest to anyone concerned with ionospheric radio propagation.

The Sun has inspired stories, myths and religions since the very earliest times. This is not surprising since it dominates the daytime skies. It is a sphere of mostly ionised gas and is about 4.5 billion years old. The Earth is about 150 million kilometres away from the Sun, and even at this distance it supplies an energy level of about $1.36kW/m^2$.

Overall the Sun is composed of 90% hydrogen, 9% helium, and the remaining 1% is made up from heavier trace elements.

## Solar interior

The Sun is around 333,400 times more massive than the Earth and contains over 99.85% of the mass of the whole Solar System. This has prompted one comment that the solar system consists of a star and some debris. Although fundamentally a gaseous body, the Sun is held together by tremendous gravitational forces that reach colossal values at its centre.

The internal regions of the Sun have a complex structure but it has still been possible for solar scientists to gain a good understanding of some of the processes that occur. Research is ongoing all the time and, with the new techniques being employed, the understanding of all the areas of the Sun is continually growing. Nevertheless, there are still many regions that are not fully understood, although it has been possible to deduce that there are a number of different areas where different processes occur. See Fig 3.1 overleaf.

First there is a central core where the energy is generated. Once generated, energy moves outwards by radiation and convection through what is termed the *radiative zone* and through a thin interface called the *tachocline* to the convection zone. Beyond these are the *photosphere*, *chromosphere* and the *corona*.

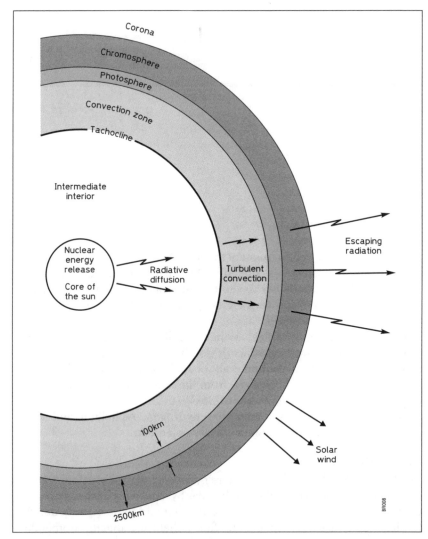

## The core

The Sun's core is the central region where the energy is generated and it forms the inner 25% of the radius of the Sun. The energy is produced as nuclear reactions convert hydrogen to helium and the amounts are colossal, with over 383 billion trillion watts of energy generated, equivalent to 100 billion tons of TNT being exploded every second. This results in temperatures in this region reaching around 15,000,000°C and, as a result of the enormous gravitational fields, the density of this region reaches about 150g/cm³ which is about 10 times that of lead.

The nuclear activity decreases towards the edge of the core which is about 175,000km from the very centre. Here too the temperature has fallen to around half the maximum value at the centre and the density is only about 20g/cm³.

## The radiative zone

This region extends outwards from the core from a distance equivalent to 25% of the radius of the Sun to about 70%. Here energy is transferred outwards primarily by radiation. Although the energy travels at the speed of light it bounces around in this area and it is estimated that it takes about a million years for the energy to reach the *interface zone* or *tachocline.*

As the gravitational forces are considerably less in this region the density falls from around 20g/cm$^3$ to around 0.2g/cm$^3$ which actually less than that of water. Also the temperature falls from around 7,000,000°C to around 2,000,000°C.

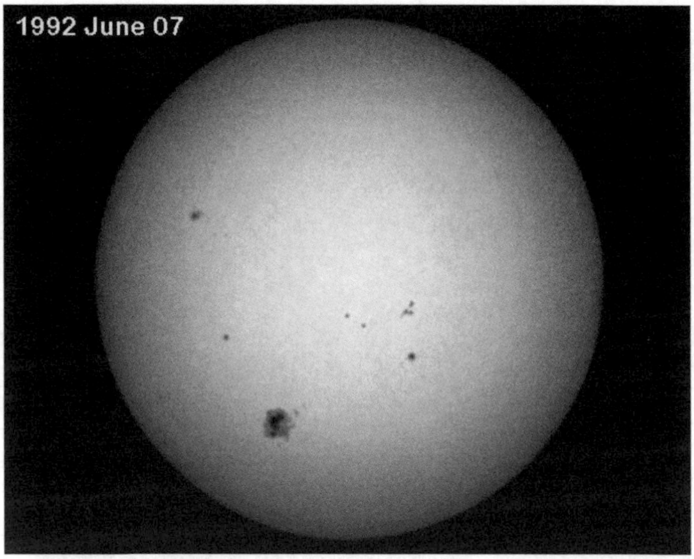

1992 June 07

Fig 3.2. A view of the photosphere. Note that it is darker towards the edge and lighter in the middle where, looking directly at the Sun it is possible to see deeper in to the hotter regions. Also note the sunspots. *(Image courtesy NASA)*

## The tachocline

This layer is also known as the *interface zone* as it acts as an interface between the radiative zone and the convection zone. The two layers transfer energy in very different ways, and the fluid motion of the convection zone above the tachocline disappears to match the more stable material conditions of the radiative zone.

The other important feature of this zone is that it is now thought that the Sun's magnetic field is generated here. It is believed that shearing flows across the layer can stretch the magnetic lines of force and enhance them. In addition to this, there appear to be sudden changes in the chemical composition across the layer.

## The convection zone

This is the outermost layer of the interior region of the Sun. The temperature across the tachocline remains almost constant and therefore the temperature at the inner areas of the convection zone is around 2,000,000°C. This falls to around 5700°C at the visible surface of the convection zone. These falling temperatures result in many of the heavier ions such as carbon, nitrogen and oxygen retaining their electrons. As a result the material becomes opaque and this makes it more difficult for the heat to be transferred. Consequently the layer starts to 'boil' and then movement occurs as convection takes place.

## Photosphere

It is actually the photosphere that forms the visible surface of the Sun (Fig 3.2). This region or layer is not a solid surface and is actually only about

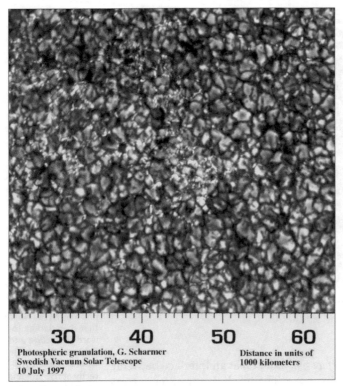

Photospheric granulation, G. Scharmer
Swedish Vacuum Solar Telescope
10 July 1997

30    40    50    60

Distance in units of
1000 kilometers

**Fig 3.3. The granules can easily be seen here on the surface of the Sun. (*Image courtesy NASA*)**

100km thick. Also, being gaseous, it is possible to see through it when looking at the centre of the Sun with the right equipment. It is for this reason that images of the Sun look darker around the edges than in the centre where the hotter deeper regions are viewed.

**Warning: The Sun is exceedingly bright and should never be viewed directly, even with dark glasses, as many people have been blinded by doing this.**

When viewing the surface of the Sun it is possible to see a number of features, including the *granules* and *supergranules* at the surface of the convection zone (Figs 3.3 and 3.4).

These granules are the result of the motion within the convection zone where the denser, lower-temperature material moves around as hotter material moves to the surface as a result of convection.

### The chromosphere

This layer is an irregular layer that exists above the photosphere. In this region hydrogen emits a reddish light as a result of an increase here in temperature to around 20,000°C.

### Corona

The Sun's corona (Fig 3.5) can be found beyond the chromosphere. It is effectively the Sun's outer atmosphere and can be seen during eclipses as an area surrounding the Sun. Within the corona, gases become heated to a temperature of around 1,000,000°C, and at these temperatures the dominant elements of hydrogen and helium atoms become completely stripped of their electrons. Other elements, including carbon, nitrogen and oxygen, fare similarly although calcium, being much heavier, does manage to retain its electrons.

These highly ionised elements generate light emissions with well-defined spectral lines. For many years astronomers had wondered where and how they were created. It was only the development of new equipment that enabled the true origin to be discovered.

In view of the large temperature difference between the chromosphere and the corona there is a sharp transition region. This separates the very hot corona at around 1,000,000°C from the chromosphere at around 20,000°C.

## Sun's rotation

The Sun rotates on its axis and has a rotation period normally taken to be about 27 days. However, as the Sun is a gaseous body it does not all rotate at the same speed. The equatorial regions are faster, taking about 24 days to complete a revolution, whereas the polar regions take over 30 days. The rotation speeds and times can be judged by monitoring the sunspots and other features that may appear on the surface.

Additionally the axis of rotation of the Sun is tilted at an angle of 7.25° to the axis of the Earth's orbit, and this means that more of the solar north pole is seen in September and its south pole in March.

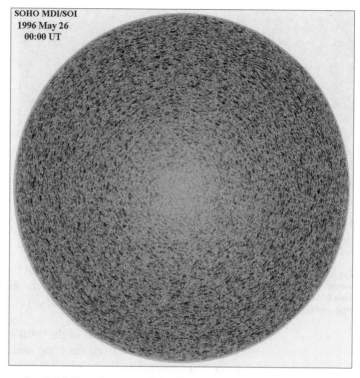

Fig 3.4. The enormous supergranules can be seen relative to the whole surface of the Sun. *(Image courtesy NASA)*

Fig 3.5. An image of the solar corona with streamers and plumes extending out into space *(Image courtesy NASA)*

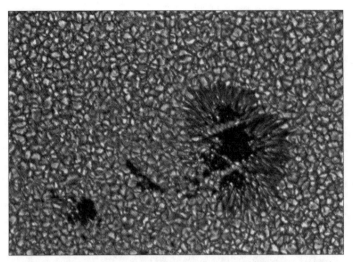

Fig 3.6. An image of a sunspot on the surface of the Sun. (Image courtesy NASA)

## Sunspots

A feature of the Sun that is of great important to radio signal propagation is the dark spots or *sunspots* that appear on its surface (Fig 3.6). They play a major role in determining the state of the ionosphere because associated with them is an increase in the level of solar radiation.

The spots have been observed for many years. It is known that the ancient Chinese civilisation observed them many years prior to the birth of Christ. However, it was not until the early 17th century after Galileo had invented the telescope that he was able to observe them more closely by projecting an image onto a piece of paper – several of his original sketches are still in existence today.

It was not until the middle of the 18th century that records of sunspot numbers were kept on a regular basis and, as the numbers varied significantly and apparently in a random fashion, it took some years before the sunspot cycle was noticed. After observing the Sun for almost 20 years and mathematically analysing the result, a scientist named Schwabe discovered the cyclical variation of the sunspots, publishing his findings in 1843. Today further research has revealed many more details about these spots, but there is still plenty that scientists are keen to discover.

Sunspots are transitory and may last for anywhere between a few days to a few weeks or even months. They appear dark as the temperature on the surface there is only about 3700°C compared to the remainder of the photosphere that is at around 5700°C.

Sunspots are first seen as a very small dark spot called a *pore*. Not all these pores develop into full spots, but the ones that do steadily develop over a period of hours or days to become full spots. As it becomes larger a lighter area is seen around the dark spot. The dark spot itself is referred to as the *umbra* and the lighter area around it is the *penumbra*.

Sunspots often appear in clusters. Each spot can be anywhere between a few hundred miles in diameter to large ones which may be almost 100,000 miles across. The groups themselves can contain several large spots and may be over a quarter of a million miles in diameter.

The spots arise from very intense magnetic fields that exist below the surface of the Sun. These fields change during the course of the cycle. At the solar spot minimum the magnetic fields are longitudinal, running from the Sun's north to its south. As the Sun rotates the fields rotate at a different speed, the equatorial regions spinning more slowly than the poles. This causes distortion of the fields that slowly align in an east-west direction. As a result of these changes the activity on the Sun varies in a cyclical form, having a distinct trough and peak.

At times the changes in the magnetic fields cause eruptions to take place through the Sun's surface. Around the eruptions the surface temperature falls dramatically, giving rise to what are seen as dark spots.

The area around the spot has a large temperature differential, and there is also a large disturbance in the magnetic field. The magnetic fields are unusually strong, with strengths many thousands of times that of the Earth's, and this results in enormous forces being produced. When a group of spots appear, one cluster will have a positive or north magnetic field and the other has a negative or south magnetic field. The field is the strongest in the darker part of the spot and weakest on the lighter part.

Large levels of electromagnetic energy and cosmic rays emanate from around the spots and this affects the levels of ionisation in the ionosphere.

## Sunspot numbers

It can be imagined that different astronomers with different equipment will arrive at different numbers of sunspots. Shortly after the discovery of sunspots Rudolf Wolf, who was the director of the Zurich observatory, devised a system giving the relative sunspot activity. This could then be used as a common standard for all observatories. The activity is defined in terms of a *sunspot number*, which is not the actual number of sunspots which are seen.

$$R = k(10g + s)$$

where $R$ is the Wolf number for sunspot activity, $k$ is a correction factor to take account of the equipment and observer characteristics, $g$ is the number of sunspot groups and $s$ is the number of observable spots (whether individually or in groups).

This formula weights the sunspot activity number heavily towards clusters. This may appear to be incorrect, but Wolf chose to adopt this system because he deduced that the large clusters were a better indication of sunspot activity than short-lived spots on their own. Despite its shortcomings, it is still a very useful indicator because sunspot numbers have been measured in this way for over 200 years and it gives very useful comparisons and visibility of trends over the whole period.

The day-to-day numbers of sunspot activity vary widely. In order to view the trends the data is averaged or smoothed over a wider period. Two stages are used for this. First the daily numbers are averaged over the period of a month and then the monthly figures are smoothed over a 12-month period. In order to ensure that the mean falls right in the middle of the month in question, rather than between months, the period of smoothing is run over 13 months, but taking half the value for the months at either end:

$$R_s = \frac{\frac{1}{2}R_{m1} + R_{m2} + R_{m3} + \ldots + R_{m11} + R_{m12} + \frac{1}{2}R_{m13}}{12}$$

where $R_s$ is the smoothed sunspot number and $R_{m1}$ to $R_{m13}$ are the monthly averaged numbers for months 1 to 13.

Both the monthly average sunspot numbers and the smoothed values are

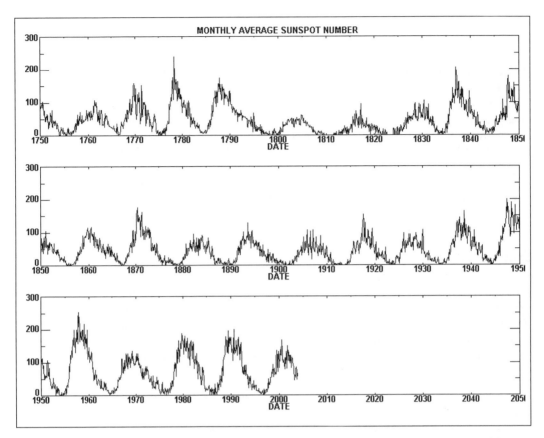

**Fig 3.7. The sunspot cycle since records began** *(Image courtesy NASA)*

available for use in propagation predictions, although the smoothed figures are much in arrears. The numbers are now prepared by the Sunspot Index Data Centre in Brussels from information supplied by a number of observatories. They appear in DX propagation information available from a wide variety of sources including the RSGB. The 12-month smoothed sunspot number correlates quite closely with the prevailing HF radio propagation conditions.

## Sunspot cycle

Once the numbers were smoothed a trend was detected and it could be seen that there was cyclical variation with a period of about 11 years. These cycles are now given numbers starting with cycle 1 which began in 1755. Since then there have been over 20 more with cycle 22 ending in the latter part of summer 1996 (Fig 3.7).

A number of factors have become obvious from analysis of the figures since the first records were available. The first is that the cycles are by no means very regular. Although the average cycle length when measured as the time between two peaks is about 10.9 years, it varies anywhere from just over seven years to 17 years. The smoothed sunspot numbers also vary widely. The maximum sunspot activity numbers vary from 49 to 200 with an average of just over 100. The minimum number can be anywhere between zero and 12.

Usually after the sunspot minimum sunspot activity rises sharply, reaching the peak in around four years, and after this it falls away more slowly, taking around seven years to decay. Naturally this figure too varies very widely and it can only be taken as a very rough guide.

The sunspot cycle is of great interest to anyone using the HF portion of the radio spectrum. Propagation conditions are greatly influenced by sunspot activity, and accordingly they vary in line with the sunspot cycle. At the low point of the cycle, the high-frequency bands above 20MHz or so may not support ionospheric reflections, whereas at the peak of the cycle frequencies at 50MHz and higher may be reflected.

## Ionospheric indicators

The number of sunspots which are seen at any time gives a guide to the amount of radiation being received by the ionosphere. Although the sunspot number can be calculated, a more objective method of achieving this is to look at the amount of radiation coming from the Sun. Not only does the Sun emit vast quantities of heat and light, it also emits energy at radio frequencies. An indication of solar activity can be made by measuring the level of solar noise. This is normally taken at a frequency of 2800MHz (a wavelength of 10.7cm) and is called the *solar flux*. It has been shown that it follows the daily sunspot number and a number of relationships have been devised. One of the most straightforward is that:

$$\text{Solar flux} = 73.4 + 0.62R$$

where $R$ is the daily sunspot count.

## Solar wind

There is a constant stream of material that emanates from the Sun. This *solar wind* streams off it in all directions at colossal speeds of up to 400km a second (about a million miles an hour). The actual source of the wind is the corona where the temperature is so high that the gravitational forces of the Sun are overcome and the material escapes. The exact method by which the material is accelerated to such colossal velocities is not yet understood. The level of the wind is affected by a number of factors and is increased in some directions when there are solar disturbances.

The solar wind reaches the Earth and, as mentioned in the previous chapter, it is deflected around the Earth by its magnetic field under most circumstances. However, under conditions where there are solar disturbances this can create geomagnetic and ionospheric storms on Earth.

## Solar disturbances

With such enormous levels of energy and high temperatures, it is hardly surprising that there are periodic disturbances on the Sun. These disturbances can be of truly enormous proportions, with vast quantities of material being flung out into the solar system along with tremendous increases

**Fig 3.8. A solar flare (Image courtesy NASA)**

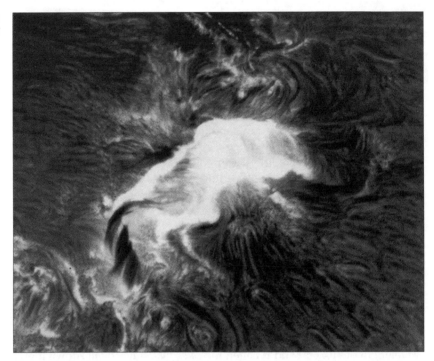

in the level of radiation being emitted. This can have a serious effect on the Earth, resulting in major changes in radio propagation conditions along with other effects such as auroras, the Northern and Southern Lights.

## Flares

Solar flares are enormous explosions that occur on the surface of the Sun (Fig 3.8). When they occur they radiate huge amounts of energy, and larger events also eject large amounts of material mainly in the form of protons into outer space. They erupt in a matter of just a few minutes, heating material to millions of degrees kelvin and ejecting colossal amounts of it from the surface of the Sun. They occur near sunspots, usually along the dividing or neutral line between areas of oppositely directed magnetic fields.

The key to understanding and predicting solar flares is the structure of the magnetic field around sunspots. If this structure becomes twisted and sheared then magnetic field lines can cross and reconnect with the explosive release of energy. When this occurs an eruption of gases takes place through the solar surface, and it extends several tens of thousands of miles out from the surface of the Sun. The gases from within the Sun start to rise and the area becomes heated even more – this causes the level of visible radiation and other forms of radiation to increase. Although the actual mechanism is not fully understood, material may break through the surface of the Sun, following the magnetic lines of force.

Initially high-velocity protons travelling at around a third the speed of light are ejected, then after about five minutes lower-energy particles follow. This material follows the arc of the magnetic lines of force and returns to the Sun, although some material is ejected into outer space especially during the larger flares. For most flares it is mainly the increase in radiation that affects the Earth. This radiation covers the electromagnetic spectrum and includes ultra-violet, X-rays and cosmic rays as well as radio-frequency emissions. In fact the radio-frequency radiation can be heard distinctly on the VHF bands as an increase in the level of background noise.

Flares generally only last for about an hour, after which the surface of the Sun returns to normal, although some post-flare loops remain for a while afterwards. The flares affect radio propagation on Earth and the effects may be noticed for some time afterwards.

Flares are classified by their intensity at X-ray wavelengths (1–8Å). The X-ray intensity from the Sun is continually monitored by the National Oceanic and Atmospheric Administration (NOAA) using detectors on some of its satellites. Using this data it is possible to classify the flares. The largest flares are termed *X-class flares*. M-class flares are smaller, having a tenth the X-ray intensity of the X-class ones. C-class flares have a tenth the intensity of the M-class ones.

In view of the fact that flares are associated with sunspots, their occurrence correlates well with the sunspot cycle. Accordingly there are significantly more around the peak of the sunspot cycle.

## CMEs

Another form of disturbance that takes place on the Sun is known as a *coronal mass ejection* (CME). These disturbances are huge bubbles of gas that are threaded with magnetic field lines, and the bubbles are ejected over the space of several hours. For many years it was thought that solar flares were responsible for ejecting the masses of particles that gave rise to the auroral disturbances that are experienced on Earth. Now it is understood that CMEs are the primary cause.

CMEs can only be observed by looking at the corona around the Sun. Prior to the space age this could only be done during an eclipse. As these occur relatively infrequently, and only last for a few minutes, CMEs were not seen until spacecraft could monitor the Sun from space. Using a *coronagraph*, a specialised telescope with what is termed an *occulting disk*, enabling it to cut out the main area of the Sun and only view the corona, it was possible to observe the activity in the coronal area. This enabled CMEs to be discovered and then monitored. Although ground-based coronagraphs are available, they are only able to view the very bright innermost area of the corona. Space-based ones are able to gain a very much better view of the corona extending out to very large distances from the Sun, and in this way see far more of the activity in this region.

It is now understood that CMEs disrupt the steady flow of the solar wind, producing a large increase in the flow. This may result in large disturbances that might strike the Earth if they leave the Sun in the right direction.

CMEs are often associated with solar flare eruptions but they can also occur on their own. Like solar flares their frequency varies according to the position in the sunspot cycle, peaking around the sunspot maximum and

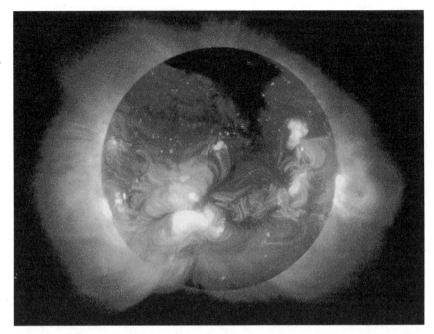

falling around the minimum. At solar minimum there may be about one each week while at the peak two or three may be observed each day. Fortunately they do not all affect the Earth. Material is thrown out from the Sun in one general direction and only if this is on an intersecting trajectory will it affect the Earth.

### Coronal holes

Coronal holes are another important feature of solar activity (Fig 3.9). They are regions where the corona appears dark. They were first discovered after X-ray telescopes were first launched into space and, being above the Earth's atmosphere, they were able to study the structure of the corona across the solar disc. Coronal holes are associated with 'open' magnetic field lines and are often, although not exclusively, found at the Sun's poles. The high-speed solar wind is known to originate from them and this has an impact on ionospheric radio propagation conditions.

In the following chapters it will be seen how the Sun affects the ionosphere, and how this enables radio signals to propagate around the Earth. However, the state of the Sun is of particular interest because it governs the level of ionisation and the overall state of the ionosphere, and hence ionospheric radio propagation conditions.

# CHAPTER 4

# Propagation near the ground

One form of radio wave propagation that is widely used on the LF and MF portions of the spectrum is the *ground wave*. It is ideal for relatively short-distance propagation on these frequencies and is used by broadcast stations on the long and medium wavebands to achieve their coverage during the daytime. Sky-wave ionospheric propagation on these frequencies is not possible during the day due to the attenuation of the signals caused by the D region in the ionosphere. In view of this, stations need to rely on ground-wave propagation to achieve their coverage.

A ground-wave signal is made up from a variety of constituents. If the antennas are in the line of sight then there will be a direct wave as well as a reflected signal. In addition to this there is a *surface wave*. This tends to follow the curvature of the Earth and enables coverage to be achieved beyond the horizon. It is the sum of all these components that is known as the 'ground wave'.

Beyond the horizon the direct and reflected waves are blocked by the curvature of the Earth and the signal is purely made up from the diffracted surface wave. This why propagation via the surface wave is commonly called 'ground-wave propagation'.

## Surface wave

The signal spreads out from the transmitter along the surface of the Earth. Instead of just travelling in a straight line the signals tend to follow its curvature. This is because currents are induced in the surface of the Earth and this action slows down the wavefront in this region, causing it to tilt downwards towards the Earth as shown in Fig 4.1. With the wavefront tilted in this direction it is able to curve around the Earth and be received well beyond the horizon.

**Fig 4.1. A surface-wave signal**

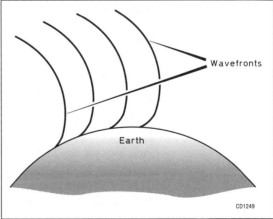

Wavefronts

Earth

CD1249

**Fig 4.2. A typical medium-wave broadcast antenna**

The degree of attenuation of the surface-wave signal is dependent upon a variety of factors. Frequency is one of the major determining factors as losses rise with increasing frequency. As a result it makes this form of propagation impracticable above the bottom end of the HF portion of the spectrum (3MHz). Typically a signal at 3.0MHz will suffer an attenuation that may be in the region of 20 to 60dB more than one at 0.5MHz dependent upon a variety of factors in the signal path, including the distance. In view of this it can be seen why high-power HF broadcast stations may only be audible for a few miles from the transmitting site via the ground wave.

The surface wave is also very dependent upon the nature of the ground over which the signal travels. Ground conductivity, terrain roughness and the dielectric constant all affect the signal attenuation. In addition to this the ground penetration varies, becoming greater at lower frequencies, and this means that it is not just the surface conductivity that is of interest. At the higher frequencies this is not of great importance, but at lower ones penetration means that ground strata down to 100m may have an effect.

Despite all these variables, terrain with good conductivity gives the best results. Thus soil type and its moisture content are of importance. Salty sea water is the best, and rich agricultural or marshy land is also good. Dry sandy terrain and city centres are by far the worst. This means sea paths are optimum, although even these are subject to variations due to the roughness of the sea, resulting on path losses being slightly dependent upon the weather! It should also be noted that in view of the fact that signal penetration has an effect, the water table may have an effect dependent upon the frequency in use.

The type of antenna has a major significance. Vertically polarised signals are subject to considerably less attenuation than horizontally polarised ones. In some cases the difference can amount to several tens of decibels. It is for this reason that medium-wave broadcast stations use vertical antennas, even if they have to be made physically short by adding inductive loading. Ships making use of the MF marine bands often use inverted-L antennas as these are able to radiate a significant proportion of the signal that is vertically polarised.

Some sky-wave signals may also be present at distances that are typically towards the edge of the ground-wave coverage area, especially at night when the D layer attenuation is reduced. This may serve to reinforce or cancel the overall signal, resulting in figures that will differ from those that may be expected.

# CHAPTER 5

# Ionospheric propagation

**S** ignals that are radiated from an antenna travel out in a variety of directions, and some will travel upwards towards the ionosphere. Unlike the ground wave that travels along the ground, the signals that travel upwards towards the ionosphere are termed *sky waves* for obvious reasons. Generally sky waves below frequencies of around 20 to 30MHz are 'reflected' by the ionosphere and returned to Earth, and hence signals may be heard from around the globe.

The ionosphere has been used to provide global communications since shortly after the beginnings of radio. Marconi's first transatlantic transmission in 1901 used very low frequencies and forms of ionospheric propagation. Then in the 'twenties the possibilities of using the short-wave (HF) bands started to be investigated and exploited. Radio amateurs made the first transatlantic contact in 1923, and then in 1925 the first trans-globe contacts were made from the UK to New Zealand. Alongside these experiments commercial interests, and in particular the Marconi Company, were investigating the possibility of using these frequencies for long-distance communications. The short-wave bands were used increasingly for all forms of applications from broadcasting to professional communications, and of course they were also widely used by radio amateurs.

Today, it is also possible to use satellites to achieve worldwide communication. They provide a more reliable form of communication because they are not subject to the changes and variations of the ionosphere but they are considerably more expensive to install and maintain, and additionally equipment may not always be available. This means that the short-wave bands combined with ionospheric propagation still have a major role to play in today's communications for professionals and amateurs alike.

## Ionospheric layers

The different regions of the ionosphere and their formation have already been described in Chapter 2. Each of these regions, namely the D, E, and F regions, act on radio signals in different ways, attenuating and refracting them. The C region has such a low free electron density that it has no effect

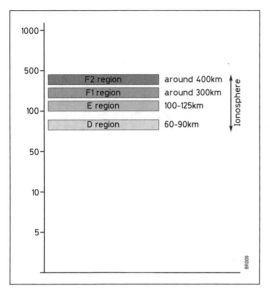

BR009

**Fig 5.1. Relative positions of the D, E and F regions in the ionosphere**

on radio signals and will not be discussed further.

### D region

The D region is the closest ionised region to the surface of the Earth that has an effect on radio signals. In view of this it is the first region that a terrestrial signal encounters on its passage to the ionosphere. It primarily acts as an attenuator to signals in the MF and HF portions of the radio spectrum. In the case of signals in the VLF portion of the radio spectrum, it does not act primarily as an attenuator but instead the same way as the E and F regions, where signals are reflected, or more correctly refracted, back to Earth in a manner described later.

The signal attenuation occurs because the radio signals cause the free electrons in the D region to vibrate in synchronism with the frequency of the signal. As they vibrate they collide with gas molecules around them. At each collision, a small amount of energy is released and this is lost from the signal itself. Accordingly it can be seen that the level of attenuation is proportional to the number of collisions that take place. In turn this is dependent upon a number of other factors.

The first is the number of gas atoms and molecules that are present. The air density at the altitude of the D region is still high when compared to other regions in the ionosphere. As a result a relatively high number of collisions occur.

A second factor is the level of ionisation. The C region, for example, has a very much lower level of ionisation, and as a result the effect it has is minimal despite the higher air density in this region.

Finally the frequency has a major bearing. As it increases so the displacement of the electron vibrations decreases, and with this the number of collisions falls. This means that a greater number of collisions occur at low frequencies when the displacement caused by the radio signal is greater. Even so, high-frequency signals still suffer some attenuation. The actual level of attenuation falls as an inverse square law, ie doubling the frequency reduces the level of attenuation by a factor of four.

Mathematically these points can be summarised by stating that the attenuation is proportional to the electron density times the electron/neutral (molecule or atom) collision frequency.

In practical terms the level of attenuation is sufficient to prevent signals in the MF portion of the spectrum from reaching the higher layers. However, at night when the ionisation in the D region falls away, they are able to reach the higher layers and signals from further away may be heard. This is evident on the medium-wave band and higher frequencies where the signals are absorbed by the D region.

## E region

Signals that enter the E region are affected in a somewhat different manner. As before, signals excite the free electrons into vibration but the density of the air is very much reduced and the number of collisions that occur is significantly less. As a result a different effect is noticed. Rather than the electrons colliding with neutrals and dissipating energy they tend to re-radiate the signal. However, as the signal moves to an area of a different electron concentration its direction is changed in much the same way that occurs when a signal passes through an area of changing refractive index. In fact the direction of the signal is refracted away from the area of the higher electron density.

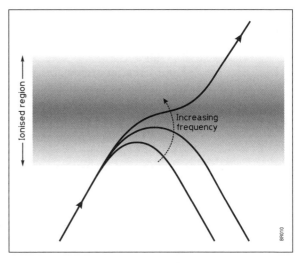

The degree of refraction is often sufficient to enable the signal to be returned to Earth, and in this case the signal is often considered to have been reflected. The degree of refraction is dependent upon a number of factors. One major factor is the degree of ionisation – the greater the level of ionisation, the greater the effect. It is also frequency dependent and higher frequencies are affected less. As the frequency increases, so the signal penetrates further into the layer until it is eventually able to pass through.

It is also found that the angle of incidence is important. Signals that have a low angle of incidence to the ionosphere only require a small degree of refraction to be returned to Earth. Those with a much higher angle of incidence need a much greater degree of refraction. As a result signals with a high angle of incidence enter further into a particular region or layer before being refracted back to Earth, and may even pass straight through (Fig 5.3).

Although the major effect of the E region is to reflect signals, the air density, particularly in the lower reaches, is sufficiently high for a significant number of collisions between free electrons and neutrals to occur. As a result there is still some attenuation experienced.

**Fig 5.2. Refraction of a signal as it enters an ionised region**

**Fig 5.3. Signals with a high angle of incidence require a greater degree of refraction and enter further into the ionised region. They may even pass straight through**

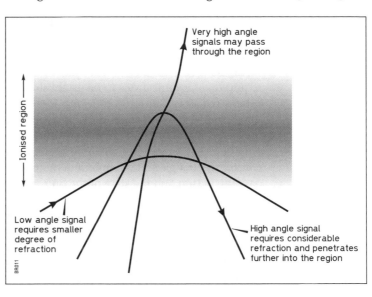

Typically at night when the E region ionisation is low this can result in figures of around 10dB per reflection for signals at around 2MHz.

### F1 region

The F1 region occurs above the E region. It acts as a reflector of signals and, as the air density is very low at its altitude, the level of attenuation is small, unlike the lower areas of the E region. Rather than being a distinct region that sees a maximum electron density that falls off above and below it, the F1 region appears as more of a 'ledge' or inflection point and is often referred to as such.

In terms of propagation it is less important than the F2 region that exists above it.

### F2 region

The F2 region is the most prominent ionised region in the atmosphere, as well as being the most important one for long-distance communications. This arises for two reasons. The level of ionisation is by far the greatest of the regions in the ionosphere, and secondly it is the highest in altitude. Having the highest electron density means that it is able to return signals that are higher in frequency to Earth, and also having the highest altitude means that distances that can be achieved are greater.

The region is also characterised by large irregularities. It is therefore not possible to analyse it on a small scale with distances of less than a few kilometres. Even on the large or global scale it presents difficulties to those trying to make forecasts of conditions. The variabilities are not all accounted for by the solar and geomagnetic changes. It possesses a 'climate' of its own, and the changes that occur also influence the way it affects radio signals. These changes make predictions for radio propagation conditions difficult but they are still made and are valuable as statistical indications of the likelihood of the conditions.

## Frequency dependence of propagation

The way in which the ionospheric regions respond to signals depends on a variety of factors. One of the major factors is the frequency of the incident signal, so a careful choice of frequency or band is required to enable the required communications to be established. In order to see how the ionosphere reacts to signals at differing frequencies it is useful to consider a signal first at the bottom end of the spectrum and see the changes as the frequency is gradually increased. However, any analysis of this form should only be seen as a very rough guide because the nature of the ionosphere is constantly changing. It is dependent on many factors, including the time of day, the season and the state of the Sun, including the position in the solar sunspot cycle.

Take a signal in the MF portion of the radio spectrum. Typically this might be a medium-wave broadcast transmission. During the daytime this will be absorbed by the D region and no detectable levels of signal are able to reach the higher regions of the ionosphere and be returned to Earth. At night, as the level of ionisation in the D region disappears, the signals are

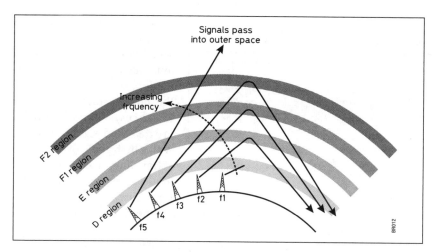

Fig 5.4. Ionospheric signal propagation at different frequencies

able to reach the very much reduced E region or the F region and be reflected back to Earth. Although the signals still undergo some attenuation by the lower reaches of the E region they are still audible, and this why interference levels on the medium-wave band increase dramatically at night as stations from further afield can be heard.

As the signal frequency is increased during the day, the level of attenuation introduced by the D region starts to fall. Typically around frequencies just above 2–3MHz signals start to penetrate the D region and reach the E region where they are reflected back to Earth. They will be audible at much greater distances than are possible via the ground wave. It should be noted that signals are attenuated during each passage through the D region.

As the frequency is increased further the level of attenuation introduced by the D region falls, and signal strengths start to rise. Additionally the signals will penetrate further into the E region and finally they will pass through, reaching the F1 region. Here again they will be reflected back to Earth, and then as the frequency rises still further they will reach the F2 region.

Eventually a point is reached where the signal has such a frequency that none of the layers is able to reflect it and return it to Earth. At this point, and at higher frequencies, it will pass through all the regions of the ionosphere and on into outer space.

## Angle of incidence and distances achievable

The angle at which a signal reaches the ionosphere is of great importance. Signals reaching the ionospheric region almost parallel to the contours will need little refraction to return them to Earth. Those reaching the regions with almost vertical incidence will require a much greater degree of refraction.

Signals that are attenuated by the D region achieve a lower degree of attenuation if the path length within the D region is as short as possible (Fig 5.5). This means that signals entering the D region almost parallel to it will be attenuated more than those that enter with an angle nearer to the vertical.

The distances that can be achieved are also dependent upon the angles at

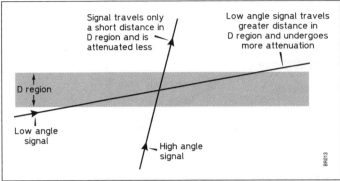

Signal travels only a short distance in D region and is attenuated less

Low angle signal travels greater distance in D region and undergoes more attenuation

D region

Low angle signal

High angle signal

BR013

**Fig 5.5. Signals that are subject to attenuation receive a lower level of attenuation if they travel in the D region for as short a path as possible**

which the signals travel. From basic trigonometry it can be seen that if a signal leaves the antenna at a low angle of radiation, ie almost parallel to the Earth's surface, then the distances achieved will be greater than signals leaving with a high angle of radiation, ie travelling at a much steeper angle upwards towards the ionosphere. Also, the higher the ionospheric region that is used, the greater the distances that will be achieved. See Fig 5.6.

Even relatively small increases in the angle at which the signal leaves the antenna can considerably reduce the distances that can be covered. The maximum distance that can be achieved using the E layer is generally considered to be 2000km (1250 miles), but this is reduced to just 400km (250 miles) if the angle is 20°. Similarly the maximum distance achievable using the F2 layer reduces from around 4000km (2500 miles) to just under 1000km (600 miles).

In order to be able to place the maximum amount of energy where it is required, it is necessary to have a directional antenna. All antennas radiate more energy in some directions than others, and their radiation pattern can be plotted out in what is termed a *polar diagram* (Fig 5.7). To ensure the optimum performance, the antenna should be orientated in the correct direction and it should have the correct angle of radiation. In many applications where the maximum distance is required, an antenna with a low angle of radiation is needed although, particularly for low frequencies that may be affected by the D region attenuation, this means that it travels through this region for longer and will suffer greater levels of loss. Not all applications require a low angle of radiation. Broadcast stations in particular will arrange for their antennas to have the correct angle of radiation so that the signal has the optimum elevation to reach the required target area.

**Fig 5.6. Effect of angle of radiation and ionospheric regions on the distances achieved using ionospheric propagation**

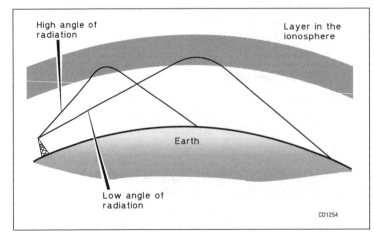

High angle of radiation

Layer in the ionosphere

Earth

Low angle of radiation

CD1254

## Skip distance and skip zone

When signals travel from a transmitter to the ionosphere and are reflected back to Earth where they can be heard, the distance from the transmitter to the receiver is known as the *skip distance*, ie the distance that the signal has skipped.

There is also an area where it is not possible to hear the signal. This arises because the sky-wave signal may not be reflected back to Earth until some distance away from the transmitter. This can happen because signals travelling upwards at a high angle towards the ionosphere may pass straight through. As a result only those signals at lower angles are reflected back to Earth, and the first signals to be returned may be well beyond the range of the ground wave. As a result there is an area between the maximum range of the ground wave and the area where the first sky-wave signals are heard where no signal may be audible. This area is known as the *skip zone* or the *dead zone* (Fig 5.8).

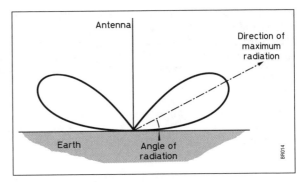

**Fig 5.7. Polar diagram plot for a typical vertical antenna**

## Critical frequency

The ionosphere is in a constant state of change. Accordingly it is very useful to be able to take measurements that give an indication of its current condition. One measurement that can be made relatively easily is known as the *critical frequency*. This is the frequency at which a signal that is directed vertically upwards just stops being reflected by a particular region in the ionosphere and passes on to the next region or into outer space. It is the highest frequency that can be reflected by a particular region.

The critical frequency is given the designation $f_o$. The subscript letter 'o' indicates that it applies to an *ordinary wave*. The ordinary wave is a wave that is reflected at the same height as it would be in the absence of the magnetic field. It is often termed the *O wave*. In contrast there is also an *extraordinary wave* that is affected by the magnetic field.

Each region has its own critical frequency, and this gives an indication of the state of the ionosphere. The critical frequency for the E layer is given the designation $f_oE$, while for the F2 layer it is designated $f_oF2$ etc. As might be expected, it varies from place to place and according to the time of day.

**Fig 5.8. The skip or dead zone where no signal is audible**

The critical frequency is measured by sending a radio pulse directly up into the ionosphere and monitoring the returned signal from a receiver co-located with the transmitter. The pulse is steadily moved up in frequency and readings taken

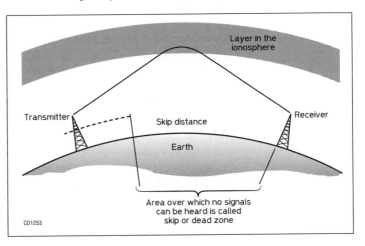

**Table 5.1. MUF factors for various distances assuming representative heights for the principal ionospheric regions**

| Region or layer | Distance (km) | | | |
|---|---|---|---|---|
| | 1000 | 2000 | 3000 | 4000 |
| Sporadic E | 4.0 | 5.2 | — | — |
| E | 3.2 | 4.8 | — | — |
| F1 | 2.0 | 3.2 | 3.9 | — |
| F2 Winter | 1.8 | 3.2 | 3.7 | 4.0 |
| F2 Summer | 1.5 | 2.4 | 3.0 | 3.3 |

over the relevant part of the spectrum. Initially a signal is returned and monitored. The time delay between the transmission of the pulse and its reception is used to determine the effective height (called the *virtual height*) of the region.

As the frequency is increased the signal is no longer reflected and passes through to the next region. Here it is initially reflected but as the frequency is again increased it eventually passes through. This process is repeated for all the regions and eventually the signal passes through the whole of the ionosphere and no reflection is received. The graphical data of the reflection height against frequency can be plotted to give what is termed an *ionogram* (see Chapter 7).

## Maximum usable frequency

At any given time there is a maximum frequency that can be used to communicate between two locations by ionospheric propagation alone. Above this frequency signals pass through the ionosphere or may be reflected in a different way so that communication is not possible. This is known as the *maximum usable frequency* (MUF).

The fact that there is a maximum usable frequency most commonly results from the situation that as the transmission frequency is increased the signal penetrates further into the ionospheric layers until it passes straight through. When the point is reached where communications can just start to fail this is the maximum usable frequency. As a rule of thumb it is generally three (for the F region) to five (for the E region) times the critical frequency and it is true for low angles of incidence, although more exact methods are available for determining this figure.

It may be calculated from the relationship:

$$\text{MUF} = F/\sec \theta$$

In this relationship, $\theta$ is the angle the incident ray makes with a vertical line through the point of incidence. The factor $\sec \theta$ is called the *MUF factor* and it is a function of the path length if the height layer is known. By using typical figures for the heights of the different ionospheric regions, the factors shown in Table 5.1 may be determined.

In some instances it may be necessary to restrict the MUF to a particular ionospheric mode. When this is necessary the values may be quoted together with an indication of the relevant mode, eg F2 MUF etc. In some instances reference may also be made to the ordinary and extraordinary waves. It is normally implied that figures are for the ordinary wave, but an X may be added, eg F2 MUF (X), for the extraordinary wave.

An *operational MUF* is also defined and may be seen in literature. This is the MUF that would permit acceptable operation of a radio service between given terminals under specific working conditions. In this definition the emphasis is on the operational acceptability of the circuit. It means that factors such as the antenna, power levels and such like are considered and gives an indication regarding the possibility of real communication at a given station.

## Lowest usable frequency

Another parameter that is of great importance is known as the *lowest usable frequency* (LUF). If the frequency of a signal is reduced, then its strength at a receiving station will fall. This results from a variety of factors. One is obviously that the D region attenuation increases, and in addition to this the signal will be reflected by lower regions in the ionosphere and this may result in further reflections and hops being required. Each reflection will introduce some loss. The overall effect is that there is a minimum frequency that will support communication between two stations.

The LUF is actually defined as the lowest frequency that would permit acceptable performance of a radio circuit by signal propagation via the ionosphere between given terminals at a given time and under specific working conditions. From the definition it can be seen that the LUF is dependent upon factors apart from the ionospheric propagation. Transmitter power, antenna gain and location, receiver characteristics and noise conditions all play their part. The type or mode of transmission is also important because wider bandwidths are required for transmissions such as SSB than for narrow-band modes like Morse or data communications. In view of the operational nature of the definition, it means that two stations located very close together, but having different equipment, may have very different figures for the LUF.

It is possible to reduce the lowest usable frequency by changing factors such as the transmitter power or by employing a different mode of transmission that enables the receiver bandwidth to be narrowed. Antennas and the like may also be changed but this is unlikely to be feasible as a short-term measure. As a very rough guide, improving the circuit by about 10dB will reduce the LUF by about 2MHz.

A further point worth noting is that the LUF actually increases in periods of high solar activity. This is caused by the fact that the increased levels of solar radiation give rise to higher levels of ionisation in the D layer. This in turn increases the level of attenuation introduced by this layer. This means that at the peak of the sunspot cycle there is degradation in the performance of the low-frequency bands for long-distance communications.

## Optimum working frequency

It can be seen that over a very short period of time, the best frequency to use would be one close to the MUF. This offers the lowest levels of attenuation and usually the best overall performance. However, the changes in the ionospheric conditions over a period of time mean that it is unlikely to be reliable and a slightly lower frequency will be able to provide a more reliable service.

To account for this an *optimum working frequency* (OWF) is defined. The term *fréquence optimum de travail* (FOT) is also used and the abbreviation is possibly more commonly found than OWF. The OWF or FOT is the lower decile of daily values for the operational MUF at a given time over a given period, normally a month. In other words it is the frequency that is exceeded by the operational MUF for 90% of the time during the stated period. Here the emphasis of the definition is on the operational aspects of communication, rather than a broad figure indicating only the state of the ionosphere.

## Path losses

There are many ways in which losses are introduced into signals that are propagated. The major one that has already been mentioned is the loss arising from the D region and in some instances from the lower regions of the E region.

Loss also arises from the fact that the signal spreads out as it travels, and the area covered by the wavefronts on the signal increase in area and accordingly the signal decreases in intensity.

Normally it might be expected that the distance travelled by the signal is that of the great circle distance between the transmitting and receiving stations. However, this is not exactly the case because the signal does not follow the curvature of the Earth but travels up to the ionosphere and then returns downwards again. As a result the distance that is travelled is larger than the great circle distance. Over paths where the angle of radiation is very low, the difference may be acceptably small but over other paths, where the angle of radiation from the antenna is much higher, there can be a significant difference. Accordingly higher levels of loss than expected might be experienced.

A further degree of loss is introduced by the fact that the polarisation of the signal can be changed by the ionosphere. Even though the signals that enter the ionosphere from terrestrial antennas are normally linearly polarised, the action of the ionosphere with the Earth's magnetic field results in the signal that emerges being elliptically polarised. Normally this loss is grouped together with a variety of other small losses. Its degree varies according to a number of factors, including the geomagnetic latitude, the season, time of day and the length of the signal path. Typically this loss may be around 9dB.

## Fading

Fading and signal variations are a major feature associated with ionospheric propagation. The signal variations may be fairly shallow, with the signal changing in level between 10 and 20dB, or it may result in the signal completely disappearing. There are a number of reasons for this but they all result from the ever-changing state of the ionosphere.

One of the major causes is multi-path interference. Even with directive antennas the signal will illuminate a wide area of the ionosphere. As it is very irregular, the signal will reach the receiving station via a number of paths each with different path lengths and the overall received signal is the summation of them all. As the ionosphere changes, the signals will fall in and out of phase with one another, resulting in the strength varying by a considerable degree. See Fig 5.9.

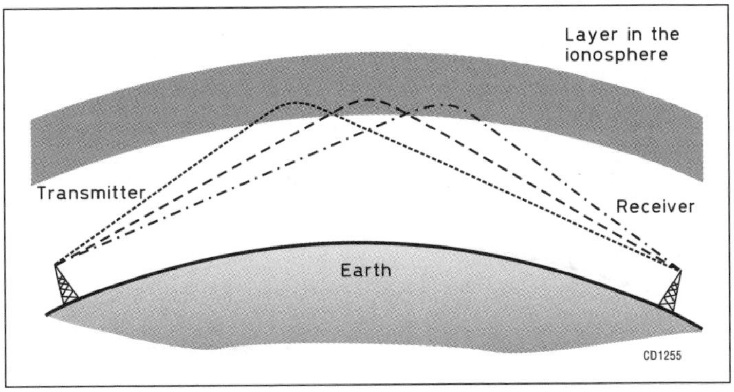

This may also be noticed on MF signals at night. Normally signals are audible via the ground wave during the day but at night the sky wave may also be audible. As the state of the ionosphere changes, so will the path length for the reflected signal, and accordingly the phase will vary. This will give rise to fading of the overall signal as the ground-wave and sky-wave signals interfere.

**Fig 5.9. A signal is received via several paths and, as changes occur in the ionosphere, signal lengths vary, causing signals to fall in and out of phase with one another. As a result the overall signal strength varies with time**

Irregularities in the ionosphere may also cause the path lengths of closely spaced frequencies to be different. For signals such as amplitude modulation (AM) and single sideband (SSB) this may result in a reduction in some frequencies in the audio range, while others are intensified. When this *selective fading* occurs serious distortion of an AM signal may occur if the carrier suffers the selective fading and a reduction in level. Since SSB signals do not depend on the transmission of a carrier, this mode is less affected by this form of fading. Additional synchronous detection of an AM signal also makes significant improvements in the signal quality under these conditions.

The fact that there are appreciable changes in density of free electrons in the ionosphere gives rise to other forms of fading apart from path length changes. In one form of fading arising from this the ability of a region to reflect a signal at a given frequency may change. When operating near the MUF the signal may fade as the signal starts to pass through the region.

There may also be regions or clouds of high electron density in the D region. Accordingly, as the clouds move signals, especially those lower in frequency, will fade as the cloud passes through the signal path. Fading of this type normally takes place over a period of half an hour to an hour and may reduce the signal by a figure between 5 to 10dB.

A further type of fading occurs when the ionosphere causes changes in the polarisation of the signal. As it changes so will the strength of the signal picked up by the antenna depending on how closely its polarisation matches the antenna polarisation.

## Multiple reflections

The maximum distance that can be achieved when using a reflection from the F2 region is around 4000km and for the other reflective regions in the ionosphere it is somewhat less. One reflection from the ionosphere does not explain how signals travel from the other side of the globe using ionospheric propagation. The reason is that signals undergo several reflections. After the signals return to Earth from the ionosphere they are reflected by the surface

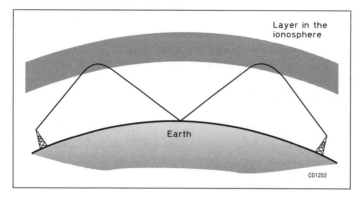

**Fig 5.10. Several reflections and 'hops' can be used to enable greater distances to be achieved**

and returned back up to the ionosphere. Here they are reflected again by the ionosphere, being returned to the Earth a second time about twice the distance away from the transmitter that a single reflection would give. See Fig 5.10.

Unfortunately the signal undergoes additional attenuation as might be expected. Each reflection by the Earth introduces some losses and therefore the signals are attenuated each time. The surface of the Earth at the point of reflection has a major effect on the level of these losses. Sea water is a very good reflector, as might be expected, but dry desert is very poor. This means that signals that are reflected in the Atlantic are likely to be stronger than those reflected by a desert region.

Apart from the reflection at the Earth's surface the signal suffers losses in the ionosphere as well. Every time the signal passes through the D region there is an additional amount of attenuation. This can be very important because the signal has to pass through the D layer twice each time it is reflected by one of the higher regions and, with more than one hop, the signal passes through the D region several times. As already mentioned the attenuation reduces with frequency. Apart from the fact that high-frequency paths are more likely to use the F2 layer and have less reflections, the high-frequency path will also suffer less loss from the D layer. This will mean that a signal on 28MHz, for example, will be stronger than one on 14MHz, assuming that propagation can be supported at both frequencies.

It should also be remembered that the path length for a multiple-reflection signal will be greater than the great circle distance around the globe, especially if high angles of radiation are used. This in itself will add to the signal loss because the loss is proportional to the path length.

## Chordal hop

At some times a tilt in the ionospheric regions, and in particular the F2 region, may occur. When this happens the signal may not be reflected back to Earth. Instead it is reflected so that it travels between the Earth and the ionosphere before meeting the ionosphere again where it can be reflected back to Earth. As this form of propagation does not involve a reflection from the surface of the Earth, the losses are much lower and accordingly signal strengths provided are higher. In some research it has been proposed that this form of propagation could account for round-the-world echoes.

The tilt or distortion in the ionosphere required to produce this form of propagation, known as *chordal hop,* occurs near sunrise and sunset and across the equator. The propagation using the equatorial anomaly generally occurs in a north-south (or south-north direction). The F2 region is higher across the equator and this means that either side of this it tilts, enabling the signals to be reflected above the Earth's surface. See Fig 5.11.

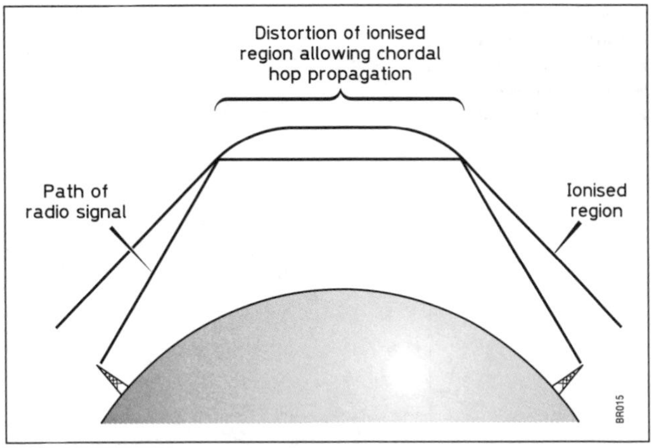

## Signal paths

There are a variety of mechanisms by which signals can propagate. With propagation over long distances the path may be a complicated summary of several hops utilising various regions. As the state of the ionosphere is not constant around the globe, reflections may use the F region in one area but the E region for signals on the same frequency in another. In some instances signals may even become trapped between the F and E regions where there is a valley in the level of ionisation, and interestingly MUFs for this mode of propagation are higher than they are for the equivalent path using a double hop.

**Fig 5.11. The north-south chordal signal path across the magnetic equator**

A form of nomenclature has been devised to categorise the various paths that can be taken. Shown in Fig 5.12 overleaf, it indicates the regions where the reflection takes place and a ground reflection is indicated by a hyphen between two letters. Thus F would indicate a single hop using the F region whereas E-F would indicate a reflection by the E region returning the signal to Earth where it is reflected back up to the F region before returning to Earth at the receiver.

## Sporadic E

One of the best-known occasional or sporadic modes of propagation is called *sporadic E* or *Es*, and can affect frequencies much higher than would be expected by normal E region ionisation. It is not uncommon for frequencies in the VHF FM band to be affected and it can extend as high as 150MHz and more on rare occasions.

Sporadic E arises when very intense clouds of ionisation form in the E region. The level of ionisation may be up to five times greater than those normally achieved at the peak of the sunspot cycle and this is the reason why signals well into the VHF region of the radio spectrum can be reflected. In view of the very high levels of ionisation, the levels of loss are particularly low and even low-power stations can be heard at good strength. See Fig 5.13 overleaf.

The intensity of the ionisation in the clouds builds up steadily, affecting first signals with lower frequencies. Then as the intensity increases so do the frequencies that are affected. The highest frequencies that may be affected vary from one 'cloud' to the next. Some may affect frequencies as high as 30MHz whereas others may affect frequencies that extend well into the VHF portion of the spectrum. It is also found that the sporadic E clouds

**Fig 5.12. Some typical signal paths that may be taken along with the nomenclature used to describe them**

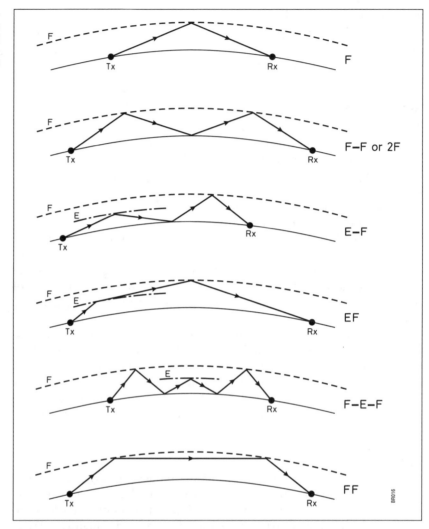

become opaque below a certain frequency, dependent upon the state of the cloud.

Those openings that occur highest in frequency, eg around 150MHz, may only be very short lived. Sometimes they may last an hour or more but at other times they may only last a few minutes. The openings that affect the higher frequencies are much less frequent than those that only affect the lower frequencies.

The sporadic E clouds vary greatly in size – they may only be a few metres across, whereas the large ones may be over 200km across. The shape also varies – some may be slightly circular in shape with approximately the same dimensions in both directions. Others may be relatively long and thin. While the shapes are not of great importance, they do help to explain why some stations may experience sporadic E propagation whereas others may not experience it or hear stations from totally different areas. They are also surprisingly thin – the normal E region ionisation is many kilometres thick but the thickness of the clouds of ionisation that give rise to sporadic E is often measured in tens of metres. The reflections occur as a result of an extremely sharp change in electron density.

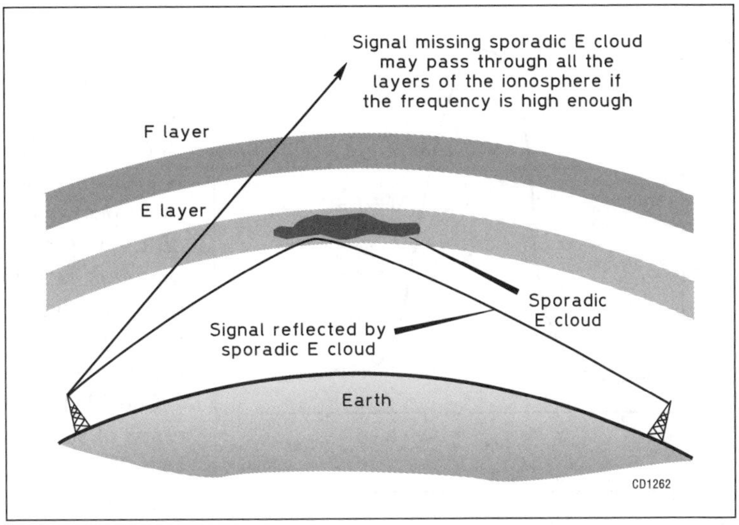

Sporadic E is not only random because of the way in which it appears, but also because once the clouds are formed

Fig 5.13. The ionosphere and sporadic E

they move as a result of the winds in the upper atmosphere. These winds reach speeds in the region of 400km per hour and can lead to any sporadic E skip changing relatively quickly. This means that the areas from which stations are heard will change and beam headings will need to be adjusted.

Sporadic E clouds appear in the lower reaches of the E region. As a result, the maximum distances that can be achieved are generally around 2000km. However, double-hop skip has been noted on a lower frequency on many occasions. This is considerably less likely on the higher frequency bands (VHF) where sporadic E propagation is less common.

Sporadic E will often enable stations well into the VHF portion of the spectrum to propagate over great distances. It also provides a means of propagation at the top end of the HF spectrum when normal ionospheric propagation may be at its ebb as a result of the sunspot cycle. However, it can degrade normal ionospheric propagation under some circumstances. The very high levels of ionisation in the clouds will reflect any signals in the HF bands reaching them. This may prevent them from reaching the higher F regions, thereby preventing them from being able to achieve much greater distances. Under these circumstances short-range signals will be detected when longer-range signals would be expected. However, the sporadic nature of the clouds and the fact that they are very mobile means that any effects are likely to be relatively short lived.

By its very nature, sporadic E is not easy to predict. However, a large amount of statistical data has been collected and from this it is possible to judge the times when it is most likely to occur. In temperate regions, ie those in the mid-latitudes between the equatorial regions and polar regions, it is found to occur mainly in summer. In the northern hemisphere the months of May to August yield the highest number of openings with a peak in June. A small peak is also noticed in December. A similar pattern is also apparent in the equivalent months, November to February, in the southern hemisphere. Generally the frequencies well into the VHF portion of the

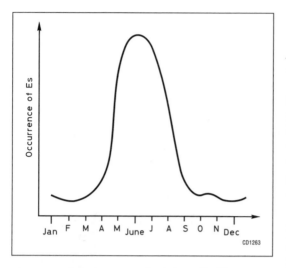

**Fig 5.14. Occurrence of sporadic E in temperature regions of the northern hemisphere. NB equivalent curves can be noted for the southern hemisphere, but changed by six months**

**Fig 5.15. The likelihood of sporadic E openings occurring throughout the day in temperature regions**

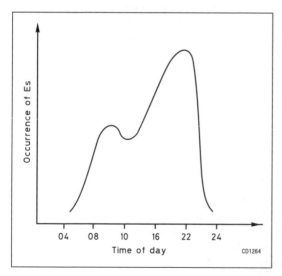

spectrum are only affected in the middle of the sporadic E season, ie mainly in June and July in the northern hemisphere. See Fig 5.14.

The time of day is also important as there is a distinct pattern to the openings. Two main peaks can be seen during the course of a day. One occurs around midday and the other is around 7pm. In the afternoon there is a slight fall in the number of openings, and in the early morning and at night there are far fewer openings. See Fig 5.15.

Outside the temperate regions, the occurrence of sporadic E is somewhat different. In both these regions there are more openings, and as a result it is thought that the way that sporadic E occurs in these regions is also different. In equatorial regions the occurrence of sporadic E is primarily a daytime phenomenon and, as might be expected because of the location, there is little difference all the year round. In polar regions what is often termed *auroral sporadic E* occurs and again there is little difference between the seasons, with it usually occurring in the morning.

The mechanisms behind sporadic E are generally not well understood and it is thought that it results from a variety of different causes. Several different phenomena produce the same or very similar effects and are all lumped together under one title. There is some evidence for believing that one type may be caused by meteors. Other proposals suggest that it is caused by electrical storms. These may extend high in altitude and there are electrical effects well above the clouds. The occurrences in the winter at night have also been linked to auroral activity. This is certainly the case for auroral sporadic E that is the result of energetic electrons entering the atmosphere from the magnetosphere. Other theories suggest that shearing forces caused by the fast-moving winds in the upper atmosphere may give rise to these intense clouds of ionisation, particularly in temperature regions. More data is being collected regarding its occurrence and this is likely to increase our understanding of this phenomenon and enable predictions to be made more accurately.

One interesting link has been noted as it appears that the sunspot cycle has some effect on temperate zone sporadic E. It has been seen that the number of openings increases during the period of the sunspot minima.

## Spread F

Under some conditions the echoes which are received back from iono-sonde soundings of the ionosphere indicate that there are irregularities in the F layer. Instead of receiving a definite echo to give the effective height of the ionosphere at that frequency, a diffused or fuzzy echo is received (Fig 5.16). This phenomenon is known as *spread F* and is very common in some areas.

When spread F occurs the F layer does not consist of a layer with a uniformly varying level of ionisation as normally seen. Instead it appears as though turbulence has broken it up into various areas of differing levels of ionisation. These each reflect signals, giving a number of paths that the signal can take. Because the signal takes slightly different amounts of time to travel the different paths, when it arrives at the receiver it is a combination of a variety of components. This results in distortion and the flutter that is characteristic of signals that have travelled via a polar route. Signal levels are also lower because this method of reflection is not as efficient as normal F layer reflections. See Fig 5.17.

Spread F occurs in two main areas. The first is around the equator between ±20° and invariably occurs at night. The second is at much higher latitudes above 40°, increasing with latitude to the extent that it is almost permanent in winter. This occurs mainly at night time but also sometimes in the day. There is little evidence of spread F occurring between latitudes of 20° and 40°.

The regions affected by spread F may occur in patches as wide as several hundred kilometres. The patches drift horizontally at speeds of around 100m per second, always drifting eastwards in equatorial regions.

Interestingly the occurrence of spread F differs between the two regions. In equatorial regions spread F occurs on magnetically quiet days, and disappears with the occurrence of a magnetic storm. However, at higher latitudes it is linked with magnetic activity.

## Grey-line propagation

At dawn and dusk signals are able to travel over much

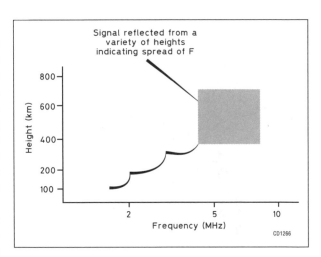

Fig 5.16. Diagram of a typical ionogram indicating the presence of spread F

Fig 5.17. The mechanism behind spread F

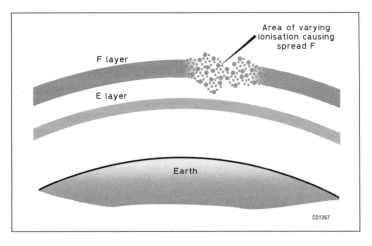

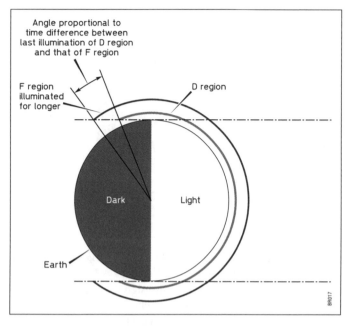

Angle proportional to
time difference between
last illumination of D region
and that of F region

F region
illuminated
for longer

D region

Dark

Light

Earth

**Fig 5.18. The F region remains illuminated for longer than the D region**

greater distances and with much lower losses than might normally be expected on some paths and frequencies. This occurs by what is termed *grey-line propagation* which occurs when signals travel along the grey or twilight zone between night and day. This area where night and day meet is also known as the *terminator*, and here signals on some frequencies are attenuated less than might normally be experienced – as a result signals can be received at surprisingly high levels over long distances.

The improved propagation conditions around the grey line occur primarily on the lower-frequency bands in the HF portion of the spectrum where the level of ionisation in the D layer is very much reduced. This occurs while the level of ionisation of the F layer, which gives most of the long-distance signal propagation, is still high.

It happens for two reasons. The first is that the level of ionisation in the D region drops very quickly around dusk and after dark because the air density is high and recombination of the free electrons and positive ions occurs comparatively quickly. The second reason is that the F layer is much higher in altitude, and as the Sun sets it remains illuminated by the Sun's radiation for longer than the D region, which is lower down (Fig 5.18). Similarly in the morning when the Sun is rising, the F region receives radiation from the Sun before the D region and its ionisation level starts to rise before that of the D region. As the level of the D region ionisation is low, this means that the degree of attenuation to which the lower-frequency signals are subjected is very much less than in the day. This also occurs at a time when the F region ionisation is still very high and good reflections are still achievable. Accordingly this results in much lower overall path losses around the grey line than are normally seen.

When looking at the radio terminator region it should be remembered that there are a variety of variables that mean that it does not exactly follow the day/night terminator as seen on the Earth's surface. The ionised regions are well above the Earth's surface and are accordingly illuminated for longer, although against this the Sun is low in the sky and the level of ionisation is low. Furthermore there is a finite time required for the level of ionisation to rise and decay. As there are many variables associated with the radio signal propagation terminator, the ordinary terminator should only be taken as a rough guide for radio signal propagation conditions.

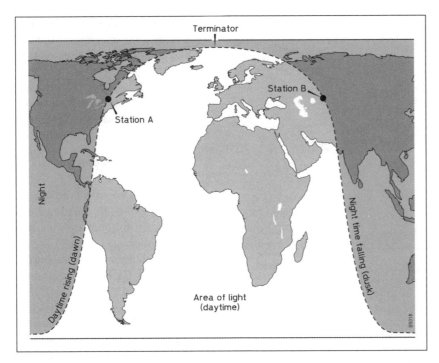

**Fig 5.19. Grey-line type propagation conditions can be seen at higher frequencies as a propagation window opens between Station A and Station B**

Frequencies that are affected by this form of propagation are generally limited to around 10MHz. This means that the bands primarily affected are the 80 (75), 30 and 30m bands. Frequencies higher in frequency are attenuated to only a minor degree by the D region and therefore there is little or no enhancement.

It is, however, still possible for higher-frequency signals to be affected by a grey-line type enhancement. This occurs when a propagation path is opening in one area and closing in another, giving a short window during which it is open on a particular frequency or band of frequencies.

Looking at the MUFs over the course of the day can demonstrate the way in which this occurs. The level of ionisation in the F layer falls after dusk and rises at dawn. This results in the MUF falling after dark. Accordingly, stations experiencing dawn find the MUF rises and those experiencing dusk find it that it falls. For frequencies that are above the night-time MUF, and for stations where one is experiencing dusk and the other dawn, there is only a limited time where the path will remain open. This results in a similar effect to that seen by the lower-frequency grey-line enhancement. See Fig 5.19.

The path of the grey line changes during the course of the year (Fig 5.20). As the angle subtended by the Sun's rays changes with the seasons, so the line taken by the terminator changes. This results from the fact that during the winter months, the northern hemisphere of the Earth is tilted away from the Sun, and towards it during the summer months. The converse is obviously true for the southern hemisphere. In addition to this the width of the grey line also changes. It is much wider towards the poles because the

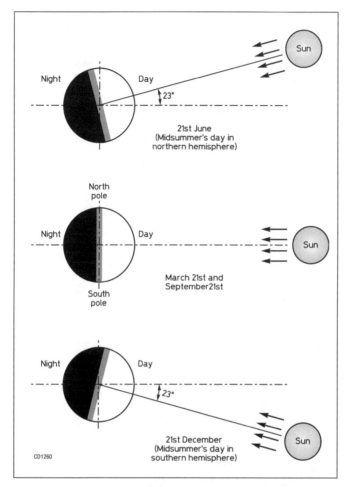

**Fig 5.20. Grey-line paths change according to the time of year**

line between dark and light is less well defined as a result of the fact that the Sun never rises high in the sky at the poles. It is also much narrower at the equator. This results in grey-line propagation being active for longer at the poles than at the equator.

## Other dusk and dawn enhancements

A number of other enhancements have been noted at dusk and dawn, although they are less well documented and investigated. At times an enhancement of around 10dB has been noted at paths that cross the terminator line at 90°. Additionally a further useful effect is that just as the band is closing or opening, competition from those stations in the area for which the band is closed will be much less, and this can be used to advantage in many instances.

## Near-vertical-incidence sky wave (NVIS)

NVIS is a very useful way in which sky-wave propagation can be used for short-haul communications. It is particularly suited to professional applications in geographical regions that are poorly served by land lines or line-of-sight repeaters, and it can provide a very useful and cost-effective alternative to satellite links. Even VHF regions in built-up or forested regions introduce very significant levels of loss, making line-of-sight VHF links virtually unworkable in many instances.

To use this form of propagation a near-vertical signal is launched towards the ionosphere at a frequency below the critical frequency. This signal is reflected by the ionosphere and returned to Earth over an area of many kilometres either side of the transmitter. In this way good local coverage can be obtained. This form of propagation is particularly useful in rough terrain because the coverage area is illuminated from above and undulations in the Earth's surface do not create shadow areas that cannot be reached.

Typically radiation should be at angles greater than 75 or 80° to the horizontal so that good local coverage is achieved. Typically coverage areas may have a radius of between 35 and 350km. The frequency needs to be

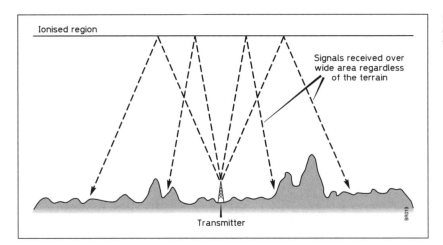

Ionised region

Signals received over wide area regardless of the terrain

Transmitter

**Fig 5.21. Near-vertical-incidence sky-wave propagation**

chosen carefully. Usually this is between about 2 and 10MHz, although during the periods of the sunspot minimum, maximum frequencies may be limited to 6 to 7MHz. By using these frequencies, the losses from the D region can be overcome, and the higher layers of the ionosphere are still able to reflect the high-angle signals without them passing right through the ionosphere.

# Ionospheric disturbances, storms and auroras

T he state of the Sun has a direct and very significant effect on the state of the ionosphere and ionospheric propagation. The solar distur- bances can cause major disruption at some times, while at other times there may be enhancements, enabling communications either to be mark- edly improved or to be established via different forms of propagation.

The way in which the solar disturbances interact with the Earth's magnetosphere and ultimately the ionosphere is very complicated. Much of it is still not completely understood but research is ongoing and pushing the frontiers of our understanding so that a much better view of the mecha- nisms involved can be gained. Nevertheless, there is still a great amount that is understood and this easily explains many of the phenomena that are observed.

## Normal conditions

Before investigating the effects of solar disturbances on the ionosphere and radio propagation, it is worth summarising the way in which the Sun interacts with the Earth's magnetosphere and the ionosphere under quiet conditions.

Radiation from the Sun strikes the ionosphere to create the different ion- ised regions that reflect the radio signals. Also there is a continual stream of material flowing from the Sun in the form of the solar wind. This is nor- mally deflected by the Earth's magnetic field so that the particles do not in general enter the atmosphere.

However, when the Sun is disturbed the quiet conditions change, and radio propagation conditions can alter in a variety of ways and for a variety of reasons. As the solar disturbances have such a major impact on iono- spheric propagation conditions they are reported in a variety of ways and by a number of different organisations. In general there are three adverse effects on the ionosphere: geomagnetic storms, solar radiation storms, and radio blackouts, corresponding to the G, S, and R designations used in the WWV report at 18 minutes past the hour. They result from an increase in the level of radiation, very-high-energy protons and finally an increase in the level of the solar wind.

## Geomagnetic and ionospheric storms

Ionospheric storms can very disruptive to ionospheric communications and can result in a complete blackout of ionospheric propagation. They occur when there is a geomagnetic storm, although not all such storms result in ionospheric storms.

All very large geomagnetic storms are now known to be caused by CMEs. Originally it was thought that they resulted from solar flares but recent research has shown this not to be the case. However, it is still true that some geomagnetic effects, including some storms, can be caused as a result of particles emitted from flares.

During a CME vast streams of particles are emitted from the Sun, and if the stream is on a trajectory that intersects with the Earth then it will have a significant impact. The stream takes between 20 and 40 hours to arrive and on Earth it is seen as a large increase in the speed and particle density of the solar wind, with the speed being the major factor in causing problems. When this increase arrives at the Earth a geomagnetic storm may occur when the level of magnetic activity changes and this can be seen by changes in the A and K indices (see Chapter 7) that can indicate the presence of a geomagnetic storm. These indices act as an indicator of the stability of the HF ionospheric propagation conditions.

The change in the magnetic activity is caused by particles entering the magnetosphere. As this happens they become trapped by the magnetic field and spiral around the lines of force between the northern and southern hemispheres, and they also drift around the Earth under the influence of the magnetic field. This motion is equivalent to a large electric current flowing around the Earth in the form of a ring. The current has an associated magnetic field that interacts with that of the Earth, giving rise to the changes known as a geomagnetic storm.

Usually the occurrence of a geomagnetic storm results in an ionospheric storm. When an ionospheric storm occurs, it changes the chemistry of the ionosphere in such a way that the levels of F region ionisation at high and middle latitudes are depressed by a significant degree. In turn this results in the maximum usable frequency reducing, often to half its value before the storm. The high-latitude E region is also affected in a similar way. There can also be an increased level of absorption in the D region levels, especially in the auroral zone.

Therefore the storm results in the maximum usable frequency falling as a result of the reduced levels of ionisation in the F region, and the lowest usable frequency rises as a result of the increased absorption. This means that the band of frequencies that can be used over a given path is greatly reduced. If the two frequencies (LUF and MUF) meet then there is a complete radio blackout and no long-distance communications are possible over that path. During a severe storm it is possible that no stations from any direction may be heard over the whole of the HF spectrum via ionospheric propagation.

The onset of an ionospheric storm is relatively gradual. Previous warning may also have been given by the occurrence of other effects such as sudden ionospheric disturbances. However, the effects of the ionospheric storm are first noticed around the poles, after which they move outwards and may affect the whole of the globe, both sunlight and dark sides. Once under way the effects of the storm may be present for several days, with the effects of some severe storms being noticeable for periods of up to a week, although such long periods are relatively rare.

In view of the solar rotation period of 27 days this provides a natural re-occurrence period for these events. As a result of this, ionospheric storms often recur at this interval, but usually with a diminished intensity. Research has shown that the effects can persist for up to 10 solar rotations on rare occasions and this factor can be kept in mind when forecasting ionospheric propagation conditions.

## Solar radiation storms

Solar disturbances may also eject vast quantities of high-energy protons. These typically take just over four hours to reach the Earth if they are on a trajectory that intersects it. As the stream of particles comes close to the Earth, the magnetic field prevents them from entering all around the atmosphere. Instead the particle stream is deflected towards the poles where they enter via the polar cap. Their entry results in a very large increase in the level of D region ionisation, and hence a much higher level of D region absorption, typically between 40 and 80dB on the lower frequencies.

This effect is known as *polar cap absorption* (PCA). The conditions appear quite suddenly and may last for up to three or four days. The PCA may totally black out radio communications across the polar cap on the lower frequencies. As it is fundamentally a D region attenuation effect, the level of attenuation falls with increasing frequency, although in view of the high levels of ionisation, the frequencies affected will be higher than those for normal D region ionisation. Users of the radio spectrum in other parts of the globe may not be aware of the blackout except that no signals are heard via polar paths across the polar cap.

## Radio blackouts

Although CMEs are responsible for the longer-term disruptions to ionsopheric propagation, solar flares can also cause disruption. One of the most commonly experienced effects of a big solar flare (M- or X-class) is a radio blackout or *sudden ionospheric disturbance* (SID). It takes just over eight minutes for the radiation from the Sun to reach the Earth, at which point the effects start to be noticed. As light takes the same time to reach the Earth, there is no prior warning of an event happening.

The radiation caused by the flare comprises all forms of radiation, including a high level of X-rays which give rise to a high degree of ionisation in the D region, with the result that there is a very significant increase in the level of D region attenuation. Although the increase in the level of radiation is rapid, it takes time for the level of ionisation to rise. Consequently the lower frequencies are affected first and, as the degree of ionisation increases, so the higher frequencies are affected. During the day the D region

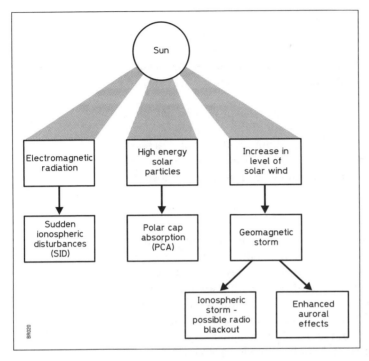

BR020

**Fig 6.1. Summary of effects caused by solar disturbances**

normally affects frequencies up to 2 or 3MHz but the increase in radiation from a flare can cause much higher frequencies to be affected. In some cases it may result in a complete blackout on the HF bands, whereas at other times only the lower frequencies may be affected.

The D region is affected by the large increase in X-rays but other forms of radiation, including ultra-violet, also increase in intensity. This gives rise to an increase in the degree of ionisation in the higher regions of the ionosphere. This can result in an improvement in conditions on the higher-frequency bands, especially at the beginning of a radio blackout when the D region attenuation is not as high.

The radio blackout conditions may last up to a couple of hours, with the high-frequency bands recovering first as the D region ionisation falls and its attenuation decreases. Also, it is only the sunlit side of the Earth that is affected. Any areas that were in darkness when the flare occurred escape the effects. A further effect of a flare is that at the same time as the X-ray radiation reaches the Earth giving rise to a blackout, noise bursts from the increased levels of radio frequency radiation may be monitored at VHF.

These disturbances are called *sudden ionospheric disturbances* because they occur without any warning. They may also be called *short-wave fades* (SWF) or the *Dellinger effect* after Dr Dellinger, who first noticed the effect and linked the degradation in propagation conditions to solar flares.

## Auroras

One of the effects that can arise from a solar disturbance is an aurora. Also known as the *Northern* or *Southern Lights* (*Aurora Borealis* or *Aurora Australis*), they are a magnificent sight in the skies. They appear as coloured glows, consisting of mainly white, green and red shades slowly changing with time. On some rare occasions a bluish glow may be seen. Sometimes the display can consist of coloured streamers that change their shape and colour over a period of a few minutes. Unfortunately these views are confined to areas around the poles, and can normally only be seen at latitudes greater than about 55°, although on some occasions when very large disturbances occur they have been seen much further away from the poles.

These displays are caused by free electrons from the increased solar wind entering the atmosphere around the magnetic poles. As the electrons descend they collide with other molecules in the upper atmosphere and release energy, some of which is light.

An aurora occurs after a CME. The arising increase in solar wind takes between 20 and 40 hours to arrive at the Earth and when it does the Earth's magnetic field diverts its particles from entering over the whole of the atmosphere. Instead they interact with the magnetosphere, causing electrons held there within the Van Allen belts to precipitate in the auroral zone areas around the poles.

The ionisation is caused in a number of ways. The free electrons that are precipitating from the magnetosphere have a very high energy and during their descent they collide with further neutrals to create further free electrons and positive ions. Typically one electron at 1keV will result in 300 free electron / positive ion pairs. In this way there are considerably more free electrons that those entering from the magnetosphere. As a result the levels of ionisation are extremely high.

Fig 6.2. A visible aurora lighting up the northern skies

In view of the very high electron densities in the polar regions it is possible for radio signals well into the VHF region to be reflected and for contacts to be made over considerable distances. The 50MHz and 144MHz bands are the main ones where auroral contacts take place, although some contacts are possible on 432MHz. However, the path is not nearly as good on 432MHz where signals are around 30 or 40dB weaker than on 144MHz. Although the path deteriorates rapidly with frequency, professional studies using ionospheric radar soundings have detected reflections, even though very weak, at frequencies in the region of 3GHz.

Auroral propagation can only take place relatively close to the poles. Generally stations must be located at latitudes greater than 55°, although

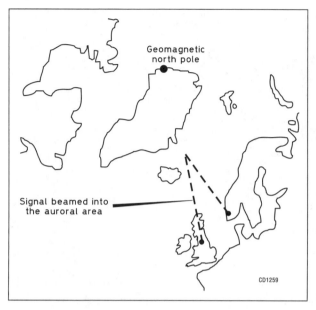

Geomagnetic
north pole

Signal beamed into
the auroral area

CD1259

**Fig 6.3. Typical beam headings required to use auroral propagation**

during large auroras stations well outside these bounds may be able to hear the effects.

To utilise auroral propagation signals should be directed toward the auroral region and not toward the station with whom a contact is to be made. This is because signals are heard by what is termed *backscatter* where the signal is reflected back in a similar overall direction to that from which it arrived. In general antennas should be pointed northwards for the northern hemisphere and southwards in the southern hemisphere so that the signal is reflected from the auroral zone or front. The optimal beam headings may vary considerably dependent upon the location of the auroral front, the station being contacted and the prevailing conditions. See Fig 6.3.

Signals that are reflected using auroral propagation are badly distorted and as a result Morse is normally the preferred mode. The distortion results from the fact that the state of the ionosphere changes very rapidly as the electrons precipitate from the magnetosphere. This causes very rapid fading to occur that manifests itself as a rough low-frequency buzz of around 50 to 60Hz. This buzz changes very much in nature from one aurora to the next, and even during the course of an auroral event.

In addition to the buzz, the signals are Doppler shifted because the electrons form a moving reflector as they stream down to Earth. This can give a frequency shift of up to 1kHz or so at 144MHz. Shifts on other frequencies are proportional to the frequency in use and are less on 50MHz and greater on the higher frequencies. Due to the fact that the electrons do not all move at exactly the same rate, there is a spread in the degree of frequency shift and this adds a form of hiss to the signal.

The combined result of the buzz and hiss means that Morse signals have a very distinctive note. It also makes single sideband signals difficult to copy. The degree of buzz and hiss is more pronounced, the higher the frequency in use, and this means that it is easier to copy single sideband signals at 50MHz than 144MHz.

It can be very useful to be able to predict the onset of an auroral event. One useful guide is known as a *pre-auroral enhancement* and occurs on the HF bands. This arises because just before an auroral event the level of ionisation in the ionosphere can rise, although this generally happens in the middle to low latitudes. It first affects the F region and this leads to an enhancement in the HF propagation conditions. After this has occurred the ionospheric storm appears. At this point the HF conditions may fail, and this is the time to look for auroral propagation in the VHF portion of the spectrum.

Further indications about the onset of auroras can be gained from the A and K indices to be described in Chapter 7. When these figures rise to the storm levels it is a good indication that a storm is likely or actually under way. These figures can be obtained from a variety of propagation-related sites on the Internet.

A further point to note is that ionospheric storms tend to re-occur at 27-day intervals corresponding to the rotational period of the Sun. Although changes in the HF conditions have been noted up to 10 rotations of the Sun, the maximum for auroral events is normally three or four times.

During an auroral event it can be seen that there are daily fluctuations that occur as a result of the normal daily changes in the ionosphere and the increase of the solar wind. Although it is not possible to set down exact rules as there are so many fluctuations there are some rough guidelines that can be mapped out. Normally events normally do not commence until around 1300 local time at the earliest. It is actually more usual for them to commence in the mid-afternoon, and continue until about 1900. After this, activity subsides and it is not normally possible to make any contacts around 2000. Later a second phase may occur between about 2100 and 2300. A third phase may then occur between about midnight and 0600 with no possibility of contacts between 2300 and 2400.

It is also found that some auroral events have no afternoon or late-evening phase, only having an after-midnight phase. When this occurs, it may herald a much larger event the following day. The times here refer to the winter daylight saving times, and adjustment should be made for the conversion from summer times at the relevant time of the year.

# CHAPTER 7

# Predicting, assessing and using ionospheric propagation

t is very important for many users of the HF portion of the radio spectrum to be able to assess and predict propagation conditions. For example, broadcasters need to know which frequencies will enable them to reach their target areas best, and this has to be planned months in advance so that frequencies can be arranged and new service schedules can be determined. For radio amateurs and short-wave listeners the conditions are of particular importance because they enable estimates of when to listen for stations from particular areas. If a beam is used, it enables the beam to be directed to areas where propagation conditions may be best supported. These and many other reasons make estimates of propagation of great interest.

To cater for all these needs various techniques are used, and a science akin to weather forecasting has been built up. Using a variety of measurements it is possible to detect the state of the ionosphere at a particular time, and using other methods it is possible to predict the propagation conditions in the future. However, like weather forecasting there are many factors that influence the state of the ionosphere and other regions that govern the way the radio signals propagate. As a result these predictions can never be totally accurate. This means that experience and the 'know-how' of the radio operator can enable the best to be made of the actual prevailing conditions.

The different portions of the radio spectrum use different mechanisms to enable signals to be propagated. Below frequencies around 30MHz the ionosphere plays a major role in the way signals propagate, but above this the troposphere and line-of-sight communications are more important. A broad summary of the propagation modes used is given in Table 7.1 overleaf.

## Amateur band summaries

There are many amateur bands located throughout the radio spectrum and several of these use ionospheric propagation. From LF through to the top of the HF portion of the spectrum there is a total of 10 bands. Even though many of them are relatively close to one another, the nature of each one is different and has its own distinct 'character'. As such it is possible to utilise

**Table 7.1. A broad summary of the propagation modes applicable to different portions of the radio spectrum**

| Band | Frequencies | Principal propagation modes |
|---|---|---|
| VLF | 3–30kHz | Ground wave, waveguide formed with ionosphere |
| LF | 30–300kHz | Ground wave, waveguide formed with ionosphere |
| MF | 300–3000kHz | Ground wave, sky wave and ionosphere (particularly E region) |
| HF | 3–30MHz | Sky wave and ionosphere (E, F1, F2 regions), also sporadic E |
| VHF | 30–300MHz | Line of sight, sometimes with tropospheric enhancement, sporadic E, meteor scatter at low end of spectrum, auroral reflections towards higher latitudes |
| UHF | 300–3000MHz | Line of sight, sometimes with tropospheric enhancement. |
| SHF | 3–30GHz | Line of sight, troposcatter |

each one in a slightly different way, enabling the best to be made of the prevailing propagation conditions.

### 136kHz (135.7–137.8kHz)

This is the only amateur band below 1.8MHz and this makes it particularly interesting. Large antennas with good earth systems are required to ensure that the antenna efficiency is raised to sufficiently high levels, as the size of antennas that can normally be erected compared to the wavelength means that efficiency levels are normally low. In view of this and the narrow bandwidth available, the transmissions that are used are always narrow-band modes. Morse code is widely used, including a variant called *QRSS* (very slow Morse). Combined with digital signal processing techniques, this enables very much lower signal strengths to be copied. Some narrow-band data modes are also used.

Using these techniques it is possible for stations to be heard commonly over distances of 100 miles or more. Beyond this, signals may be heard over distances of several hundred miles. However, occasional transatlantic contacts have been made.

### 160m (Top Band) (UK allocation 1.81–2.0MHz, US allocation 1.80–2.00MHz)

This is the lowest frequency band in what is thought of as the short-wave part of the radio spectrum, although it is in the MF portion of the spectrum rather than the HF section. In view of its status with the longest wavelength (disregarding 136kHz that was not allocated when its name was first used), it is often referred to as *Top Band*. The actual allocations between different countries vary slightly as demonstrated by the difference between the UK and US allocations. However, many other countries have significantly smaller allocations.

As the band is in the MF portion of the spectrum, signals are heard via ground wave during the day as sky-wave signals are completely absorbed by the D region. The distances that may be achieved are dependent upon a variety of factors including the transmitter powers, antennas (vertical polarisation is best for ground wave) and the nature of the terrain between the transmitter and receiver. Sandy areas are not good for propagation, whereas moist areas provide much better propagation. Signals travel best over the sea as it provides a good medium over which ground-wave signals may propagate and the signals do not need to diffract around hills (unless there are islands with hills in the signal path). In general it should be possible for signals to be heard via the ground wave over most types of terrain for distances of around 75km.

At night the D region ionisation disappears and the distances that can be achieved greatly increase. Often propagation uses the lower parts of the E region and some attenuation is introduced during each reflection. Nevertheless many signals are audible over distances of 1000km and more and often communications are possible across the Atlantic. On some occasions it is possible to establish communication with stations on the other side of the globe, although for long-distance contacts it is essential that very effective antennas are used by both stations.

Timing is very critical for long-distance contacts because the propagation paths may only be available for a short time. In some instances the openings may only last a few minutes. It is essential that the path remains in darkness to ensure that D region attenuation is not present, although there are short dawn and dusk improvements, especially for contacts with stations at the other side of the globe, which may only last for a few minutes.

For transatlantic communication, the paths may be open for several hours but they generally peak when it is sunrise or sunset at the relevant end of the path. It is also found that north-south paths generally peak around midnight.

As a general rule long-distance work improves in winter because of the longer hours of darkness and lower levels of static. Additionally the fact that radiation of the ionosphere is absent for longer means that the residual D region ionisation is lower and levels of attenuation from this and also the lower reaches of the E region are minimised.

Unfortunately winter in the northern hemisphere corresponds to summer in the southern hemisphere and this means that there is no optimum time of year for cross-hemisphere contacts and these may be undertaken during any season.

## 80m (UK allocation 3.5–3.8MHz, US allocation 3.5–4.0MHz)

As this band is higher in frequency than 160m, there is a greater possibility of long-distance contacts. During the day stations that are a few hundred kilometres distant may be heard as high-angle signals are able to penetrate the D region. Then at night as the D region ionisation falls, so the distances over which stations can be heard increase. To achieve good results, efficient antennas are required. Although it is possible to establish some long-distance communications, the high levels of static and other noise mean that good signals must be transmitted if they are to exceed the level of noise at the receiving station.

Again the long-distance paths must remain in darkness for long-distance communications to be possible, although grey-line propagation can produce some spectacular results. Here it is often possible to hear stations from the other side of the globe peaking with signal strengths that may appear to be the same as local stations. The optimum time for these contacts is during the spring and autumn. Skip can be very selective as signals may at first be completely inaudible but with stations in slightly different areas hearing the long-distance signals at good strength. Then as the skip varies signals may increase, while they fade out with the first stations to hear the long-distance signals.

In general the performance of 80m for long-distance communication improves toward the low end of the sunspot cycle. This arises from the fact that ionisation levels are lower, and in particular the ionisation of the D region is lower. This brings lower levels of attenuation for this band.

### 40m (UK allocation 7.0–7.1MHz, US allocation 7.0–7.3MHz)

This is often considered to be one of the low-frequency bands in the HF spectrum and as a result it often does not receive the attention that it deserves. In fact it can produce some surprisingly good results. During the day stations may be heard up to distances of several hundred kilometres. Distances much beyond this are not common during the day because only signals with a high angle of incidence are heard. Low-angle signals have further to travel through the D layer and they suffer greater levels of attenuation. This means that the skip zone is either very small or non-existent.

At night the D region ionisation level falls and the distances over which signals can be heard greatly increases. The strength of local stations falls as the skip distance increases and this considerably reduces the level of interference, making long-distance communications far easier. There are also considerable dawn and dusk enhancements that can be used to great advantage, and these typically last for longer than on 3.5MHz as the degree of attenuation introduced by the D region is less.

### 30m (UK and US allocations 10.100–10.150MHz)

This band was released after the World Administrative Conference (WARC) held in 1979. Although it is some years since the recommendation was made to release these frequencies for amateur communications, they are still not widely used but nevertheless the band is still capable of producing some exciting results.

The propagation is very similar to that experienced on 40m except that the level of D region attenuation is less during the day. This means that daytime propagation using lower angles of incidence can be supported and distances that can be achieved are slightly greater. It is also found that a skip or dead zone is present, except periods around the sunspot peak when D region ionisation levels will be greater.

In general, the level of absorption is less than on 40m, and during the night distances increase, providing worldwide communications. Propagation is again best when the path lies in darkness but again conditions are enhanced at dawn and dusk, although this is less much less marked than on the lower-frequency bands.

## 20m (UK and US allocations 14.00–14.35MHz)

This is the mainstay, long-haul band providing the possibility of contacts over 1500km at most times, and possibility of communications over much greater distances at some time virtually every day. Here the level of D region attenuation has generally fallen to the degree that it is not a major factor and the band offers the possibility of good long-distance contacts during the day via the F2 region.

At night, during the sunspot minimum and in the winter the band normally closes and no signals are heard because the ionisation level of the F region falls to such a degree that the MUF is below 14MHz. However, during the summer the band generally remains open for much or all of the night, especially during periods of the sunspot maximum. It is generally found that spring and autumn bring the best conditions, particularly for contacts between the northern and southern hemispheres when stations from the opposite hemisphere may be heard at various times of the day.

## 17m (UK and US allocations, 18.068–18.168MHz)

This band, which was also released by WARC 1979 for amateur use, is another useful long-haul band. It possesses many of the characteristics of the 20m band, being a mainly daytime band with the possibility of operation at night during the summer and the periods of the solar maxima. However, being slightly higher in frequency it requires that the MUFs are higher and therefore it will not always remain open as long as the 20m band.

## 15m (UK and US allocations, 21.00–21.45MHz)

This is one of the long-haul bands that has been available for very many years. As it is higher in frequency than the 20m band it may not remain open as long, but again its higher frequency means that long-haul stations can be heard at good strength. However, it is more variable and is affected by the prevailing conditions more. Near the peak of the solar cycle the band is open during the day and well into the night when stations can be heard over many thousands of kilometres. When the band is open like this, signal strengths are usually better on this band than 20m because it is higher in frequency and D region attenuation is less. However, conditions are usually not quite so good in the early morning because it takes some time for the ionisation levels to rise sufficiently to support communication. During the sunspot minimum few stations may be heard during the day and none at night because MUFs may not rise sufficiently high to support communication on these frequencies.

A good indication of the state of the band may be gained by listening to stations in the broadcast band above 21.45MHz. If no stations are audible then it is likely that no amateur signals will be heard.

## 12m (UK and US allocations, 24.89–24.99MHz)

Another of the WARC 1979 bands, this is higher in frequency than 15m and as such provides a good opportunity for daytime long-haul contacts. It is less likely to be open into the evening than 15m as it is higher in frequency and

MUFs tend to fall after dusk. As a daytime band it offers the possibility of a good number of long-haul contacts, although it is greatly affected by the solar cycle and there will be long periods during the solar cycle minimum where the band is not open except by sporadic E.

### 10m (UK and US allocations, 28.00–29.70MHz)

This band is right at the top of the HF portion of the radio spectrum. As such it is the most variable of the short-wave bands, but when it is open it offers excellent possibilities, especially for stations using low power levels or for those with poor antennas. The reason for its performance is that D region attenuation is exceedingly low and even low-angle signals are hardly attenuated.

Against this the band suffers from long periods during the solar or sunspot minima when it is completely closed to F region propagation. The only mode of propagation by which signals may be heard over any distance during these periods is by sporadic E, which occurs relatively frequently in summer months in temperate zones. In equatorial zones sporadic E is more common and appears all the year round. However, distances that may be covered by sporadic E are less than by reflection by the F region, although some double-hop propagation can occur on occasions.

## Monitoring conditions

There are a number of methods that can be used to monitor the actual conditions and state of the bands. Sounders may be used to test the state of the ionosphere but one of the most reliable methods is to monitor stations from around the world to find out to which areas the propagation paths are actually open. This can be time consuming and unreliable if undertaken in a random fashion, but a variety of beacon stations have been set up to enable propagation conditions to be monitored either on a casual or an ongoing basis.

### Beacons

There are a number of set frequencies and sub-bands within the amateur bands that are set aside for the operation of beacons. These transmit throughout the day on specific frequencies, and by monitoring the transmissions along with knowledge of their locations it is possible to gain an accurate view of the prevailing propagation conditions. This can be useful for determining which bands provide the best opportunities as well as for long-term studies of propagation.

The first beacons to be set up were allocated individual frequencies, and there is a sub-band in the 10m band that is reserved for this purpose. While the beacons are very useful, if they are on a variety of frequencies it is not always easy to gain a quick idea of propagation conditions. To provide a more effective service and to utilise less bandwidth an internationally co-ordinated network of beacons has been organised for use on the HF bands. When complete there will be 18 stations at locations around the world transmitting on frequencies of 14.100, 18.110, 21.150, 24.930 and 28.200MHz.

The beacons share the same frequency but are time multiplexed, ie they transmit at different times. In this way a receiver need only be tuned to a single frequency to discover which paths are open. Each beacon transmits in turn, with transmissions consisting of the callsign being sent in Morse code at 22 words a minute at a power level of 100W. Then one-second dashes are sent at power levels of 100W, 10W, 1W, and finally 0.1W. After transmitting this sequence, the station falls silent until its next slot in the three-minute cycle. Further information about this project can be found at http://www.ncdxf.org/beacons.html and a map identifying the current locations of the beacons is also available at this site.

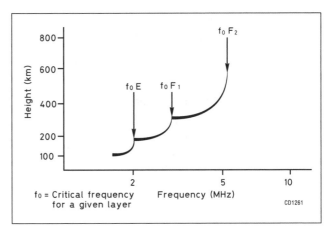

**Fig 7.1. Diagram of a typical ionogram**

## Ionosondes

It is possible to gain a view of the state of the ionosphere above by the use of an ionosonde. These instruments are often also termed *vertical incidence sounders* (VIS). There is a variety of instruments that have been used over the years from different manufacturers and with different specifications but basically they all provide the same function.

In essence the systems transmit a pulse of RF power that is radiated vertically upwards and the reflected signal is monitored and plotted on what is termed an *ionogram*. Initially the signal is reflected back by the ionosphere, but as the frequency is increased it penetrates deeper into the relevant region and eventually passes on to the next ionised region where the same process occurs as the frequency is swept upwards. Eventually a point is reached where the signal passes though all the regions of the ionosphere and it is not reflected. The resulting plot which normally uses a logarithmic scale for clarity looks something like that shown in Fig 7.1. These ionograms indicate the critical frequency for each of the regions.

There have been many developments in ionosonde technology. Analogue systems were used up until the 'seventies. These systems all swept through the relevant parts of the spectrum, normally from about 1MHz up to between 15 and 25MHz. They generally used a relatively high power level, often up to 25kW. Sweeps could take anywhere between about 30 seconds and two minutes which gave them the ability to look at relatively short-term variations in the ionosphere.

Since the 'seventies digital systems have been used. These provide essentially the same information as the analogue ones but provide considerably more facilities and they are able to manipulate the data far more easily.

Although it is possible to set up an ionosonde at almost any location required, a number of stations are located around the globe and data from many of them is stored at World Data Center A at Boulder in the USA. An ionosonde station located at Slough in the UK provided ionospheric soundings since 1935, and although it is no longer in use it provided data from the same location over six solar maxima and five minima.

## Solar and geomagnetic indicators

It is possible to obtain information about the factors that influence the ionosphere and in this way it is possible to start to forecast what conditions might be like without taking soundings of the ionosphere. There are a number of indicators that are used, including the solar flux that indicates the level of radiation being received and also the geomagnetic indices that give a view about the way in which the ionosphere might be affected by solar disturbances.

### Solar flux

This is one of the major indicators of solar activity and gives a good idea of the level of radiation that is being received from the Sun.

It is measured by detecting the level of radio noise emitted at 2800MHz (10.7cm) and it is quoted in terms of *solar flux units* (SFU). An SFU has the units $10^{-22}$ watts per square metre per hertz.

To prevent different levels being quoted by different observatories, the standard is taken as the reading taken by the Penticton Radio Observatory in British Columbia, Canada.

The solar flux is statistically related to the level of ionising radiation reaching the ionosphere, but unfortunately does not give an exact figure because the radio noise level at 2800MHz is around $10^6$ times less than the intensity of the radiation used to create the ionisation in the ionosphere. Despite this it is a good first-order approximation, particularly for the F region that is responsible for most of the long-haul HF propagation. However, the best correlation with the levels of ionisation comes from the smoothed sunspot number mentioned in Chapter 3, but by its very nature this figure is only available in arrears.

It is possible to relate the daily sunspot number to the solar flux. A number of equations are available but the one given below is one of the most straightforward and sufficiently accurate for most purposes:

$$\text{Solar flux (SFU)} = 73.4 + 0.62R$$

where $R$ is the daily sunspot or Wolf number.

A slightly more accurate, although more complicated, equation indicates the relationship between the two values is not totally linear.

$$\text{Solar flux (SFU)} = 63.7 + 0.728R + 0.00089R^2$$

Solar flux values can typically range from values around 50 at the sunspot minima to around 300 for short periods around the times of maxima. Low values will naturally indicate that MUF figures will be low, whereas high values will give an indication that the MUF will possibly be much higher. For 'good' propagation conditions it should be remembered that there should

| Table 7.2. It is possible to relate the K and a indices so that approximate conversions can be accomplished between the two values | | | | | | | | | |
|---|---|---|---|---|---|---|---|---|---|
| K index | 0 | 1 | 2 | 3 | 4 | 5 | 6 | 7 | 8 | 9 |
| a index | 0 | 3 | 7 | 15 | 27 | 48 | 80 | 140 | 240 | 400 |

be several consecutive days of sustained high solar radiation with the absence of solar disturbances.

## Geomagnetic indices

The state of geomagnetic activity is critical in determining the possible state of ionospheric propagation conditions. There are two indices that are used that are related to each other. The first is the K index while the second is the A index. Although different, both these indices give indications of the severity of magnetic fluctuations, and hence the level of disturbance to the ionosphere.

The *K index* is a three hourly measurement of the variation of the Earth's magnetic field compared to what are 'quiet day' conditions. The measurement is made using a magnetometer which indicates the variation of the magnetic flux in nanoteslas. This reading is then related to the K index and, when plotted on a logarithmic scale, the curve is virtually a straight line, indicating the relationship is quasi-logarithmic.

There are many stations worldwide that measure and log the K index. As the magnetic field varies around the globe each one has its own value, dependent upon the way in which the magnetosphere is affected, and therefore it is not possible to have a simple relationship between one station and a global K index. Instead the individual K indices are averaged around the globe to give what is termed the *Kp* or *planetary K index.*

The Kp index ranges in value from 0 to 9. Values between 0 and 1 indicate quiet magnetic conditions and would give rise to virtually no degradation in HF band conditions. Values between 2 and 4 provide an indication of unsettled magnetic conditions that indicate the possibility of some degradation on the HF bands. A value of 5 signifies a minor storm and 6 a larger one. Values through to 9 indicate steadily worsening conditions with 9 representing a major storm that is likely to result in a blackout in HF conditions for several hours.

The *A index*, unlike the K index, is a linear measure of the Earth's field. As a result its values extend over a much wider range. It is derived from the K index by scaling it to give a linear value which is termed the *a index*. This is then averaged over the period of a day to give the A index. Like the K index, values are averaged around the globe to give the planetary Ap index.

Values for the A index range up to 100 during a storm and may rise as far as 400 in a severe geomagnetic storm.

Although geomagnetic and ionospheric storms are interrelated, it is worth noting that they are different. A geomagnetic storm is a disturbance of the Earth's magnetic field and an ionosphere storm is a disturbance of the ionosphere. However, a magnetic storm usually, but not always, leads to an ionospheric storm.

## Manual interpretation of data

It is often advantageous to gain an idea of what the solar flux, daily sunspot number and magnetic indices mean. For good HF conditions to prevail, one of the first requirements is that the solar radiation should be high and have remained this way for several days. This will enable the F2 region ionisation levels to rise and enable the MUFs to increase, thereby supporting good HF conditions. For this to occur, the solar flux levels should be around 150 or more for a period of several days.

It is also necessary that the levels of geomagnetic activity should remain sufficiently low during the periods of high solar flux that conditions are not suppressed and MUFs decreased as a result. Typically the Kp index should remain below a value of around 2. If this is maintained with sufficiently high solar flux levels then HF band conditions should be good.

## Propagation software

While it is possible to gain an insight into HF ionospheric propagation conditions from examining the figures manually, there are many good propagation prediction programs that are available. Many are available freely on the Internet or can be bought for reasonable sums of money. For someone seriously interested in using the HF bands they represent a good investment. A summary of the different programs available is not included here because there have been a number of reviews that have been undertaken and have appeared in the magazines. As the programs are being continually updated any information supplied here would be out of date. A search of the Internet will provide more up-to-date information.

The programs have been developed over many years and take many factors into account, and in this way they are able to provide a far better interpretation of the figures than is ever possible from a swift glance. In this way they will be able to predict which paths are likely to be open and at which times. To achieve this they normally require several elements of data to be entered. The majority of programs require the sunspot number, although some need the solar flux taken as a 90-day average (to remove the wide day-to-day variations that occur) or an average for the last seven days. In addition to this they normally require an indication of the geomagnetic activity in terms of the Ap or Kp index. Other factors include the time and date. The position of both the stations is also needed so that the path between them can be estimated. Station equipment in terms of antennas, power and the like, as well as details about the terrain, also help estimate the viability of many paths and factors such as the LUF.

These programs are very useful as they are able to take a vast number of factors into account. They are also able to present the results graphically and this greatly helps their interpretation. When used as intended they can give a very useful view of what propagation conditions are likely to be but at best they are only able to give an estimate.

# CHAPTER 8

# Tropospheric propagation

A lthough there are many radio signal propagation effects associated with the ionosphere, the troposphere also plays a very important role. It primarily affects frequencies above those affected by the ionosphere, becoming increasingly important at frequencies in the VHF portion of the spectrum and above.

## Line of sight

Most communications at VHF might initially thought to be only along the line of sight. Although under normal conditions this may be thought to be true, even under these conditions the distance that signals may be propagated is extended beyond that which a direct straight-line model might be expected to give.

The reason for this is that radio waves are refracted as they pass from a region with one refractive index to a region with another refractive index, bending towards the region of the higher index as described in Chapter 1.

The refractive index of the atmosphere varies according to a variety of factors. Temperature, atmospheric pressure and water vapour pressure all influence the value. Even small changes in these variables can make a significant difference because radio signals can be refracted over the whole of the signal path and this may extend for many kilometres.

An example of the effect that the changing refractive index of air has on electromagnetic waves can often be seen with light waves. Hot air above a heated surface such as a road or even sand directs the light upwards so that light from the sky is seen. As the hot air moves this creates a shimmering effect that can be easily noticed. A proper mirage can occur if cool air falls below a region of hot air. In this case the light waves are refracted downwards and this extends the line of sight. Tales are told of oases that appear in the desert as a result of this!

Radio waves are also electromagnetic waves and are affected in exactly the same way. There are very small changes in refractive index in the air as a result of slightly increased pressure closest to the Earth's surface and also

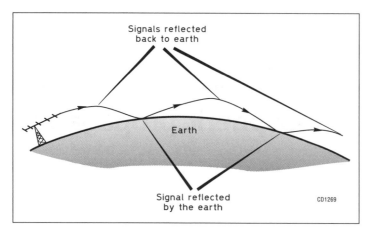

Signals reflected
back to earth

Earth

Signal reflected
by the earth

CD1269

**Fig 8.1. Signals may be refracted back to the Earth's surface which will then reflect them back upwards to give a form of multi-hop transmission**

as a result of the higher level of water vapour. As a result the radio signals are refracted around the Earth's surface.

The average value of refractive index is around 1.0003, but it can easily vary from 1.00027 to 1.00035. In view of the very small changes that are seen, *N units* are often used. These N units are obtained by subtracting 1 from the refractive index and multiplying the remainder by a million. In this way more manageable numbers are obtained.

$$N = (\mu - 1) \times 10^6$$

where $\mu$ is the refractive index.

As a rough guide the value of refractive index falls by around 0.0004, ie 400 N units, with every kilometre increase in height. This occurs under normal conditions and in a temperature zone. As a result it means that radio signals will be bent slightly towards the Earth's surface and will be able to follow its curvature beyond the geometric horizon. The actual values extend the radio horizon by about a third. This factor is used in most coverage calculations for broadcast radio transmitters.

## Enhanced conditions

It is possible for the troposphere to provide enhanced propagation conditions that enable signals to be heard over much greater distances than would normally be possible. This form of 'lift' in conditions is less pronounced on the lower portions of the VHF spectrum, but becomes an important means of communicating over extended distances, particularly on bands including 144MHz, 432MHz and higher. Under some conditions distances of 2000km may be achieved with distances of up to 3000km on rare occasions.

These extended distances result from much greater changes in the values of refractive index over the signal path. This enables the signal to achieve a greater degree of bending and as a result follow the curvature of the Earth over greater distances

Sometimes the change in refractive index may be sufficiently high to bend the signals back to the Earth's surface. When this occurs they are reflected back upwards again by the Earth in a similar fashion to that seen with multi-hop ionospheric propagation on the HF band. In this way the signals may be considered to 'bounce' along the Earth's surface (Fig 8.1). This is one form of *tropospheric duct* that can occur.

A form of elevated ducting can also occur. This may happen when a layer of air with a high refractive index has a layer with a lower refractive index underneath and above it as a result of the movement of air that can occur under some conditions. When this happens the signals may be trapped in the elevated duct and they may travel for several hundred miles. They may also not be audible to stations under the duct and in this way create a skip or dead zone similar to that experienced with HF ionospheric propagation (Fig 8.2).

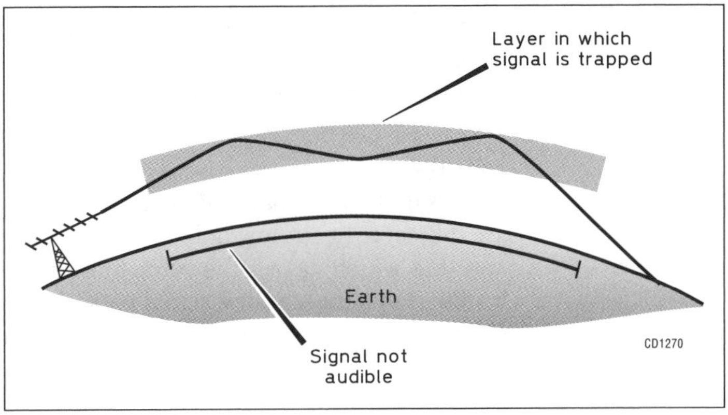

## Causes of enhanced conditions

The region of the atmosphere in which signals are affected by the troposphere is below altitudes of just 2km. As these regions are greatly influenced by the weather, it is hardly surprising to find that it has a major influence upon radio propagation conditions. By monitoring the weather it is possible to gain a good insight into what the tropospheric radio conditions may be.

Fig 8.2. Elevated ducts enable signals to travel for extended distances and are not audible to stations underneath the duct creating a dead zone for the signal

One of the major mechanisms that causes a significant change in the refractive index is a *temperature inversion*. Normally the air closest to the Earth's surface has the highest refractive index. This is caused by the fact that the air is denser in this area and it contains more water vapour. Against this the temperature is highest closest to the surface and this tends to have the opposite effect, reducing the refractive index gradient. However, when a temperature inversion takes place, the hot air rises, allowing colder, denser air to come in close to the Earth. When this occurs it gives rise to a greater change in refractive index with height and hence better propagation conditions.

Temperature inversions can arise in a number of ways. One is when an area of high pressure is present. The stable conditions mean that air close to the ground heats up and rises. As this happens, colder air flows in underneath it, causing the inversion. This effect is particularly dramatic in summer when temperatures are higher. In view of the fact that high-pressure systems are normally stable and tend to move slowly, these conditions may last for many days. Additionally the greatest improvements tend to occur as the high-pressure area is moving away and the pressure is just starting to fall.

Temperature inversions may also occur when a cold front passes by. A cold front occurs when an area of cold air meets an area of warm air, and under these conditions the warm air rises above the cold air, creating a temperature inversion. Cold fronts tend to move relatively quickly and as a result the improvement in propagation conditions tends to be short lived.

It is possible for temperature inversions to be caused by a variety of other meteorological conditions. The temperature higher above the ground is more stable than that very close to the ground. As a result frosty mornings can result in the temperature of the air close to the Earth's surface being much lower and causing a temperature inversion. After a hot day, when the Earth's surface cools rapidly, temperature inversions may arise. Another time to watch is a summer sunrise. This can give rise to a short-lived inversion, as the air higher in altitude receives the effects of the Sun's rays sooner. Also the subsidence of colder air into a valley can give the same effect.

## Fading

Signals that are propagated via tropospheric refraction over great distances are subject to deep slow fading. This is because the air is constantly moving and that which causes the refracting and ducting may be blown around, leading to changes in the signal path. As the signal will reach the receiver via several paths and is therefore the sum of several different individual signals, these may fall in and out of phase with each other, leading to changes in signal strength.

## Assessing conditions

Although it is possible to gain a good idea of what conditions may be like, it is only possible to fully assess which paths may be open by monitoring the stations that can be heard and noting the directions from which the signals are coming.

The easiest method of doing this is to monitor any beacons and also compare their signal strengths with the normal readings under flat conditions (if they are audible). Repeaters may also be useful for this but it may not always be easy as frequencies are often re-used and distant stations may be masked by more local ones.

Another useful indicator of a lift in conditions can be gained when patterning is seen on the analogue UHF television channels. This patterning indicates interference which does not normally occur because frequency planning is carefully handled when re-using television channels to ensure that interference levels are not normally noticeable. Thus when interference is noted it indicates that signals are able to propagate beyond their normal coverage areas.

It is also worth noting that not all the bands are affected equally. Some may be relatively flat while a good 'lift' is under way on another band. Also conditions may be enhanced more in one direction than another, so it is worth gaining a good idea of the best directions from an assessment of this from the beacons. In this way the beam antenna can be orientated approximately in the optimum direction.

## Band summary

Bands that are affected by tropospheric propagation are all affected to differing degrees, and in the same way that each of the HF bands had its own characteristics, the same is also true for those in the VHF, UHF and higher portions of the spectrum.

### 6m (UK allocation 50–52MHz, US allocation 50–54MHz)

This is the lowest amateur allocation in the VHF portion of the spectrum. At the peak of the solar cycle the MUFs may exceed 50MHz and under these conditions worldwide communication is possible via F2 ionospheric propagation. It is also commonly affected by sporadic E propagation, especially in summer in temperature latitudes. It is also used for meteor scatter, auroral propagation and EME (moonbounce). Being comparatively low in frequency it is not greatly affected by tropospheric effects.

### 4m (UK allocation 70.0–70.5MHz, no US allocation)

An allocation at 70MHz is only available to a few countries, and this means that few international two-way contacts can be made. Nevertheless it is affected by sporadic E and it is ideal for meteor scatter. Tropospheric effects are more noticeable than at lower frequencies.

### 2m (UK allocation 144.0–146.0MHz, US allocation 144.0–148.0MHz)

The 2m band is one of the most popular of the VHF/UHF bands, offering a variety of modes of propagation. Tropospheric propagation can enable long-distance communications to be established when weather conditions are right to provide the enhanced refraction and ducting. Other modes, including auroral propagation, meteor scatter and EME, are also applicable. This is also the highest band that is generally accepted to support propagation by sporadic E. Openings can be up to an hour or so in the summer in temperate zones.

### 135cm (No UK allocation, US allocation 222–225MHz)

This band shares many of the same characteristics as 2m. Occasionally it has been known to be affected by sporadic E.

### 70cm (UK allocation 430–440MHz, US allocation 420–450MHz)

Although under flat band conditions very-well-equipped stations may be expected to communicate over distances of around 300km, tropospheric refraction is more pronounced on this band than on the lower frequencies and it forms the main method of extended-range communications. Ducting can support contacts up to distances of around 2000km and again the all-water path between California and Hawaii has enabled extended distances of around 4000km to be achieved on a few occasions. The band also supports EME propagation. Some auroral and meteor scatter propagation may be possible at times.

### 33cm (No UK allocations, US allocation 902–928MHz)

The main way in which extended distances may be covered on this band is by tropospheric lifts and enhancements. Maximum distances tend to be around 1500km.

### Higher frequencies

As the frequencies rise, so the achievable distances tend to fall as a result of increasing path losses. Despite this, distances of around 1500km may be

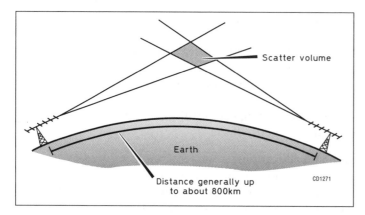

Scatter volume

Earth

Distance generally up
to about 800km

CD1271

**Fig 8.3. The mechanism by which tropo-scatter can be used**

achieved on all bands up to 10GHz. Above this frequency attenuation from atmospheric water vapour starts to become significant and, although long distances are possible, they are not as great as on the lower-frequency bands.

## Troposcatter

Tropospheric scatter is sometimes used for communications over distances of up to about 800km. It can be used almost regardless of the conditions, although signal strengths are normally very low. This means that high powers, high antenna gains and sensitive receivers are required. This method of propagation is often used commercially, normally on frequencies above 500MHz. It provides a reliable method of communication and is much cheaper than using satellites. In fact it provides much of the data communication for the oil rigs in the North Sea off the coast of the UK when they need to communicate with stations on the mainland.

This form of propagation relies on the fact that there are areas of slightly different dielectric constant in the atmosphere at an altitude of between 2 and 5km. Even dust in the atmosphere at these heights adds to the reflection of the signal. A transmitter launches a high-power signal, most of which passes through the atmosphere into outer space. However, a small amount is scattered when is passes through this area of the troposphere, and passes back to Earth at a distant point as shown in Fig 8.3. Path losses are very high, and the angles through which signals can be reflected are normally small.

The area within which the scattering takes place is called the *scatter volume*, and its size is dependent upon the gain of the antennas used at either end. In view of the fact that scattering takes place over a large volume, the received signal will have travelled over a variety of paths. This tends to 'blur' the signal and make high-speed data transmissions difficult.

It is also found that there are large short-term variations in the signal as a result of turbulence and changes in the scatter volume. As a result, commercial systems employing this type of propagation use multiple-diversity systems. This is achieved by using vertical and horizontally polarised antennas as well as different scatter volumes (*angle diversity*) and different frequencies (*frequency diversity*). Control of these systems is normally undertaken by computers. In this way such systems can run automatically, giving high degrees of reliability.

## Attenuation by the atmosphere

In the case of transmissions in the VHF section of the spectrum, atmospheric conditions like rain and fog have little effect on the signals. However, as the frequency increases, the atmosphere has a much greater effect on the level of attenuation in the signal path and at certain frequencies the loss introduced has to be considered.

For most UHF communications the effects of rain and moisture in the atmosphere are not significant as far as additional path loss is concerned. However, as the frequencies rise above about 3GHz the loss can introduce an additional degree of variation into the path. As may be expected, the loss is dependent upon the amount of rain and also the size of the droplets. As a rough guide very heavy rain may introduce an additional loss of about 1dB per kilometre at around 5GHz, and more at higher frequencies. The loss occurs for two reasons. The first is absorption by the rain droplets. The level of actual attenuation is dependent upon the droplet size. The second occurs as a result of the signal being scattered and, although the power is not lost, not all of it travels in the original direction it was intended. In this way the antenna gain is effectively reduced.

At frequencies well above 10GHz, attenuation due to the gases in the air may be evident and in particular water vapour and oxygen. This arises by virtue of the permanent electric dipole moment of the water vapour and the permanent magnetic dipole moment of the oxygen molecule. There are peaks for the components, with an oxygen peak around 60GHz, giving rise to an attenuation of around 15dB per kilometre, and a lower peak at just over 100GHz of just under 2dB per kilometre. Water vapour losses rise steadily with frequency but peak just below 200GHz, introducing a loss of nearly 40dB per kilometre. For most amateur operation these effects are unlikely to be of any significance.

# Meteor scatter

**M**eteor scatter is a form of propagation that is used with great success by a number of people. Primarily a VHF mode, it requires specialised operating techniques and high-performance equipment, but it is nevertheless capable of enabling signals to travel over distances up to a maximum of 2000km.

Its existence as a form of propagation was discovered in the 'thirties but it took until the 'sixties before it was exploited to any degree. Now it is also employed by amateurs who can use it to great effect with high-speed Morse. Professionals find it useful for a number of data transfer applications, particularly when sending data from remote unmanned sites to a base. Its use came to the fore in the 'seventies as computers became more accessible and equipment control became more sophisticated, allowing for the systems to be controlled by computers and data to be conveniently transferred where no other suitable means was available.

This form of propagation relies on the fact that meteors enter the Earth's atmosphere and as they do so they burn up, leaving a trail of ionisation behind them. These trails typically occur at altitudes between about 85 and 120km and they can be used to 'reflect' radio signals so that they return to Earth and can be heard over great distances. However, as the area covered by the ionisation trail is small, only minute amounts of the signal are reflected and this means that high powers coupled with sensitive receivers are often necessary.

## Meteors

Meteor scatter propagation naturally relies on meteors entering the atmosphere from outer space. It is surprising to note that thousands of millions enter each day (the estimate is about $10^{12}$ meteors with a total weight of around $10^6$ grams). The vast majority of these meteors are small, and are typically only the size of a grain of sand. The number of meteors entering the atmosphere is inversely proportional to their size. For a 10-fold reduction in size, there is a 10-fold increase in the number entering the atmosphere over a given period of time. So most meteors are burnt up in the

| Table 9.1. Major meteor showers | | | |
|---|---|---|---|
| **Shower** | **Begins** | **Maximum** | **Ends** |
| Quadrantids | 1 January | 3 January | 6 January |
| April Lyrids | 19 April | 21 April | 24 April |
| Eta Aquarids | 1 May | 4 May | 7 May |
| June Lyrids | 10 June | 15 June | 21 June |
| Ophiuchids | 17 June | 20 June | 26 June |
| Capricornids | 10 July | 26 July | 15 August |
| Delta Aquarids | 15 July | 27 July | 15 August |
| Pisces Australids | 15 July | 30 July | 20 August |
| Alpha Capricornids | 15 July | 2 August | 25 August |
| Iota Aquarids | 15 July | 6 August | 25 August |
| Perseids | 25 July | 12 August | 18 August |
| Orionids | 16 October | 21 October | 26 October |
| Taurids | 20 October | 4 November | 25 November |
| Cepheids | 7 November | 9 November | 11 November |
| Leonids | 15 November | 17 November | 19 November |
| Geminids | 7 December | 14 December | 15 December |
| Ursids | 17 December | 22 December | 24 December |

upper atmosphere, and there are very few that are sufficiently large to survive entering the atmosphere and hence reach the Earth.

It is possible to split meteors into two categories: those that are associated with meteor showers at particular times of the year and those that enter the atmosphere all the time, known as *sporadic meteors.*

## Meteor showers

The fact that meteor showers occur periodically throughout the year is well known by astronomers and meteor scatter enthusiasts. These showers take place at set times of the year and last for a day or two, and during them the number of meteors entering the atmosphere rises significantly. For some of the larger showers, the number of visible trails increases markedly, allowing the casual observer to see a worthwhile number in an evening. A list of the major showers is given in Table 9.1, and of these the Perseids shower in August is probably the best.

Shower meteors are characterised by what is termed their *radiant.* This is the point in the sky from which they appear to originate. The radiant is usually identified by the name of the constellation or major star in the area of the sky from which they appear to come, and this name is usually given to the shower itself. Apart from the main showers detailed in the table, there are hundreds and possibly thousands of other showers that have been recorded, often by amateur observers.

The showers are thought to arise from comet trails and indeed most of them have been linked to specific comets. As the comets travel through the universe they leave behind them a trail of small particles that orbit the Sun in an elliptical orbit. As a result, when the Earth passes through one of these orbits, the particles in the Earth's path enter the atmosphere and produce a meteor shower. As these meteors are orbiting in a particular direction they enter the atmosphere from the same direction and as a result they appear to originate from the same point in the sky.

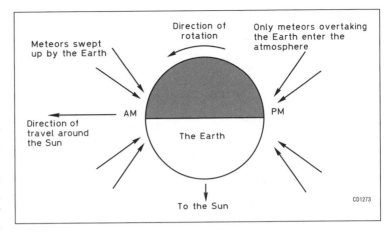

Fig 9.1. Variation of meteors over the day

## Sporadic meteors

Most meteors that enter the Earth's atmosphere are sporadic meteors. They are from the space debris that exists within the universe and in our solar system. The majority of this debris arises from the vast amounts of material that is thrown out by the Sun into the universe. Unlike the shower meteors they enter in all directions and they do not have a radiant.

Although the density of the debris in the solar system is broadly constant (after meteor showers have been discounted), the rate at which meteors enter the atmosphere varies quite considerably over the course of a day (Fig 9.1). This occurs as a result of the rotation of the Earth. Meteors are 'swept up' as the Earth's atmosphere rotates into the sunrise, but their amount falls away as it rotates away from the sunset. The same effect can be seen as an automobile is driven in rain – the raindrops hit the front windscreen but very few hit the rear window.

As a result of this effect the minimum number of sporadic meteors enter the atmosphere at around 6pm, and the maximum number at around 6am. The actual ratio between the maximum and minimum is generally accepted to be around 4:1 but the exact figure is dependent upon a number of factors including the latitude at which the measurement is taken. It is found that the effect is less distinct towards the poles.

Other factors also have an effect, including the change of the season. This can be attributed to two main factors. The first is that the distribution of sporadic meteors around the Earth's orbit is not uniform. The density is higher in the areas of the orbit that the Earth passes through in June, July and August. The other reason is related to declination of the Earth's axis. There is a 22.5° tilt of the polar axis relative to the Sun that gives rise to the different seasons, and as well as the seasonal variation in meteor rate. Those areas at right-angles to the direction of travel will receive the most meteors, whereas those at a greater angle will receive less. See Fig 9.2.

The combination of the two annual effects is that maximum-to-minimum variation is accentuated in the northern hemisphere where the two effects add together, but it is minimised in the southern hemisphere where the two effects tend to cancel each other. As might be expected, in the equatorial regions there is a crossover between the characteristics of the two hemispheres.

Finally, there is a small change of around 2:1 roughly in line with the

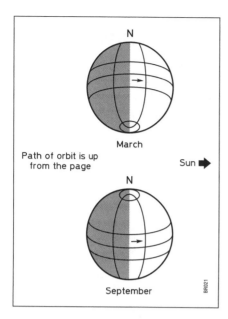

Path of orbit is up
from the page

Sun ➡

March

September

BR021

**Fig 9.2. Leading surface of the Earth in orbit at various seasons**

sunspot cycle. It appears that the number of meteors reaching the Earth reaches a peak around the trough of the sunspot cycle, ie the two effects are about 180° out of phase. This means that there is an improvement in meteor scatter propagation when the HF bands are at their minimum.

## Meteor trails

Meteor trails form as the meteors enter the Earth's atmosphere and burn up as the friction from the air rises. The meteors enter the atmosphere at speeds anywhere between about 10 and 80km a second. The trails then form in a region between about 85 and 120km in height which is around the same altitude as the E region in the ionosphere. The actual height at which a meteor burns up is dependent upon a number of factors including size, weight and the angle at which it enters the atmosphere. The greater the entry velocity of the meteor, the higher it will burn up.

When a meteor burns up it heats up to such a degree that the atoms vaporise, leaving a trail of positive ions and negative electrons. The trail is a very long thin parabola with the meteor at its head. Typically the trails are only a few metres wide but they may be over 25km long.

The level of ionisation in the meteor trail is very high, being much higher than that in the ionosphere resulting from solar radiation. This means that signals with frequencies up to about 150MHz can be reflected by these trails.

There are two types of meteor trail. One is said to be *over dense*, and the other *under dense*. The point at which they change from one type to another is taken to be an electron density of $1 \times 10^{14}$ electrons per cubic metre. This actually corresponds to a critical frequency of 90MHz. While the electron density is used to define the type of ionisation trail, it is actually the way in which a trail reacts that is of real importance. The meteors that create the under-dense trails are normally very small, often the size of a grain of sand. Those that generate the over-dense trails are usually larger. Typically meteors have to have a mass larger than about $10^{-3}$ grams with a radius of around 0.004m to create an over-dense trail. Below these approximate figures under-dense trails result.

Since over-dense trails are produced by meteors that are generally larger than those required to produce under-dense ones, they are less frequent, although they give relatively 'strong' reflections. Having a high electron density, signals do not completely enter over-dense trails and they are reflected. These reflections have a slow rise to the peak strength and a slow decay (Fig 9.3). Their overall duration is generally a few seconds but, during the period of the reflection, the signal undergoes multi-path related effects that affect their performance for the very high data rate transmissions normally used for professional applications. Nevertheless they are ideal for amateur contacts.

Under-dense ones act in a very much different way. Having a lower electron density, the signal penetrates the trail and it is scattered rather than being refracted. In this way some of the signal is returned to Earth. Again the portion of the signal that is returned is very small and very efficient systems are required. The reflected signal typically rises to a peak strength in a few hundred microseconds and then decays. This may take between a few hundred milliseconds to as long as a few seconds. This decay is attributed to the spreading and diffusion of the trail's electrons.

Of the two types of meteor ionisation trail, it is normally the over-dense type that is used for amateur radio communications and the under-dense ones for commercial communications. The reason for this is that the requirements for the two types of communications are somewhat different.

## Frequencies

Like other forms of propagation, meteor scatter is dependent upon the frequency in use. This affects a number of parameters: reflected power levels as well as the burst duration. The levels of power returned reduce significantly with increasing frequency, as does the effective duration of the trail. As a result the maximum limit for meteor scatter operation is generally around 150MHz, although some very dense trails have been known to affect frequencies as high as 500MHz.

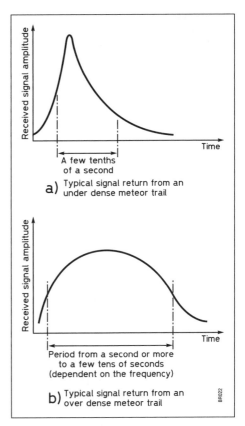

**Fig 9.3. Comparison of typical signal returns from over-dense and under-dense trails**

Most amateur meteor scatter operation takes place on 2m, although 6 and 10m also provide very good opportunities and some operation takes place on 70cm. The meteor trails last much longer on the lower frequencies, typically 10 times longer on 6m than 2m. This makes operation on the lower frequencies much easier, although the higher antenna gains that can be achieved with reasonably sized antennas counteracts the better reflections obtainable on the lower frequencies.

For the commercial systems that use the under-dense trails the maximum frequency is somewhat lower – about 50MHz. Typically most operation takes place between about 40 and 50MHz, although operation on lower frequencies would be possible. Below 30MHz interference levels rise as a result of the increased number of signals resulting from ionospheric propagation and therefore there is little operation there.

## Paths and distances

Using meteor scatter it is possible to establish communications over distances up to just above 2000km. A minimum distance also exists because the trails are only able to reflect signals over a certain angle. As a result the

**Fig 9.4. Effect of antenna gain on meteor scatter systems**

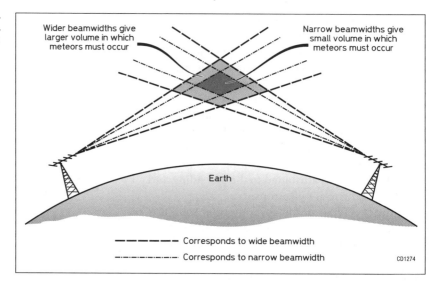

Wider beamwidths give larger volume in which meteors must occur

Narrow beamwidths give small volume in which meteors must occur

Earth

— — — — — Corresponds to wide beamwidth

—·—·—·—·— Corresponds to narrow beamwidth

CD1274

minimum distance is around 500km. Between these two figures, the optimum distance is just over 1000km.

When making contacts the optimum beam heading is around 10 to 15° to one side of the direct path as this is where most of the usable reflections can be achieved.

The gain of the antenna needs to be carefully considered because there are a number of effects to take into account. To improve the signal levels at the receiver, a high-gain antenna is desirable. However, it will have a much narrower beamwidth and the amount of the sky that is illuminated is much less. In turn this reduces the number of ionisation trails that can be used. Therefore it is necessary to determine a balance between the improvement in signal strength and the number of trails that are required. See Fig 9.4.

## Doppler shift

Meteor scatter signals are affected by a Doppler shift. This is because the point where the signal is reflected changes as the meteor moves forwards, and the trail behind it diffuses and reflection decays. This can give a shift in frequency of as much as 2kHz on the higher-frequency bands although it is correspondingly lower for the lower-frequency bands.

At higher frequencies the signals are only present for a short time, and this results in them giving an effect rather similar to a 'ping'. Signals at lower frequencies are generally present for longer and the effect is not nearly as noticeable.

## Operating techniques

Meteor scatter requires a number of specialised operating techniques. The fact that communication can only be maintained in short bursts while the trail supports a reflection means that information must be transferred very quickly in both directions and procedures must be very efficient. Single sideband is rarely used because it takes too long, although it is employed occasionally on 6m. The more common way is to use very-high-speed Morse. Speeds of 400 words a minute are used to enable sufficient amounts of information to be transferred during the life of a meteor trail. This is generally generated and read by computers these days. Previously tape recorders were used to speed up and slow down the signals for transmission and reception. Additionally contacts are often pre-arranged to enable stations to be listening on exactly the right frequency at the right time. It is essential to know the exact frequency because of the very-short-term nature of the signals, and accordingly there is no time to tune around the band for suitable ones. Furthermore any random contacts are normally made on the specific meteor scatter channels.

Although highly specialised meteor scatter stations are not needed for this mode, there are some basic requirements. Contacts can be made on 6m with relatively low power because the reflections are good at this frequency. On 2m where higher levels of ionisation are needed to affect the signals, the reflections are much shorter and higher power levels are needed. Typically power levels of around 100W at the antenna and an antenna gain of just over 10dB are needed. Coupled to this, a low-noise front-end is essential because of the low signal strengths at the receiver. In addition to this a means of sending and receiving high-speed Morse code is required.

## Commercial operation

Meteor scatter is used for many commercial systems, although the increasing availability of satellites means that this form of communication is being used less. Despite this, it provides a very convenient method over distances of just over 1000km where real-time communication is not required and for less cost than a comparable satellite system. For example, it may be used for returning data that has been collected by a sensor of some sort at a remote site. It may take 15 to 30 minutes or possibly even more to send data as it is necessary to wait for suitable meteor trails. If large amounts of data need to be sent then longer delays may be expected.

For a meteor scatter system it is necessary to set up two stations. One of these sends out a probe signal while the other monitors the frequency. When a suitable trail appears, the receiving station picks up the probe signal and sends a reply. Data is then transferred in packets, the receiving station sending out acknowledgements after each packet. When the trail fades and communication is lost, the probe signal is sent out again until another usable trial is detected.

This form of propagation is easy to install and operate, especially now that computer technology to control the system is cheap and easy to use. It also has the advantage that it is reliable from day to day and not subject to the variations of the ionosphere.

# CHAPTER 10

# Space communications

T here is plenty of scope for communications using the Moon and satellites that orbit above the Earth's atmosphere. Satellites are widely used today and are able to provide very effective communications. There is also the possibility of propagation using the Moon as a passive reflector. Both these forms of communication are able to provide very useful means of propagating signals over distances well beyond the line of sight.

## Satellites

Since the early 'sixties when satellite communication became an economic reality its use has considerably increased. Not only are satellites used for applications such as communication, but also for direct broadcasting, weather forecasting, geological investigations navigation (GPS) and much more. Whatever their use, there are a few fundamental concepts that are common to all satellites.

### Satellite orbits

One of the main features of any satellite is its orbit. Its use and other technical requirements will govern the optimum type of orbit, and in turn this will determine many aspects of the make-up of the satellite.

To look at the different orbits it is first necessary to understand the different forces working on satellites. They are pulled in towards the Earth by the gravitational field, and to balance this they orbit the Earth at a speed that creates a centrifugal force that is equal and opposite to the gravitational force. Simple physics dictates that the lower the orbit, the stronger the gravitational field and therefore the faster the satellite has to orbit the Earth to balance the forces. Similarly, higher orbits mean that the satellite does not need to travel so fast. For a very low orbit of around 100 miles a velocity of about 17,500 miles per hour is needed and this means that the satellite will orbit the earth in about 90 minutes. At an altitude of 22,000 miles a velocity of just less than 7000 miles per hour is needed, giving an orbit time of about 24 hours.

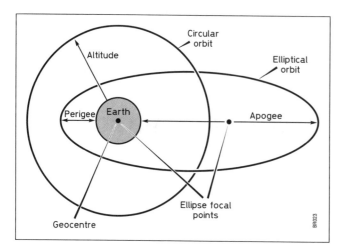

Fig 10.1. Satellite
orbits

There are two main types of orbit that can be chosen for a satellite. The most obvious is a *circular* orbit, where the altitude of the satellite remains constant. The second is an *elliptical* one where the height varies with the position on the orbit.

One of the most popular types of orbit for many professional communications and direct broadcast applications is a *geostationary* orbit where the satellite rotates in the same direction as the rotation of the Earth and has a 24-hour orbit period. In this way it revolves at the same angular velocity as the Earth and in the same direction, which has the advantage it remains above the same position on the Earth's surface. To achieve a geostationary orbit it must be above the equator and have an altitude of 35,860km (22,300 miles).

There are a variety of altitudes that can be used for satellite orbits. Many are in what is termed a *low earth orbit* (LEO) having orbit times of 90 minutes or more, while others are much higher. Between altitudes of around 1000 and 25,000km the environment is not suitable for most satellites as the Van Allen radiation belts between these altitudes cause considerable damage to electronic equipment. Accordingly satellites are normally stationed below or above these altitudes.

There are a number of terms associated with satellite orbits. Any orbit, whether circular or elliptical, forms a plane that passes through the centre of gravity of the Earth (the *geocentre*). The rotation direction around the Earth can also be categorised. If the satellite is rotating in the same direction as the rotation of the Earth then it is said to be *posigrade* or if it is in the opposite direction then it is said to be *retrograde*. The path on the Earth's surface over which the satellite travels is known as the *ground track*. This is a great circle track that has its centre at the geocentre.

Satellites with equatorial orbits obviously travel around the equator but for all others there are two points where they cross the equator. The point at which the ground track crosses the equator passing from the southern to the northern hemisphere is called the *ascending node*, and the one where it crosses from the northern to the southern hemisphere is called the *descending node*. For these orbits it is usually found that the ground track shifts towards the west for each orbit because the Earth is rotating towards the east underneath the satellite.

The height and velocity of the satellites are important factors. For many calculations the height above the geocentre is required whereas it is often stated as the height above the ground itself. For these calculations the radius of the Earth is taken to be 6370km (3960 miles).

Velocity is another important factor as already seen. For a circular orbit it is always the same. However, in the case of an elliptical one the speed changes dependent upon the position in the orbit. It reaches a maximum when it is closest to the Earth and it has to combat the greatest gravitational pull, and it is at its lowest speed when it is furthest away.

Elliptical orbits have a number of further points that are of interest. An ellipse has two focal points, and one of these is the geocentre of the Earth. Additionally there are two other points, one where the satellite is furthest away from the geocentre which is called the *apogee* and one where it is closest called the *perigee*.

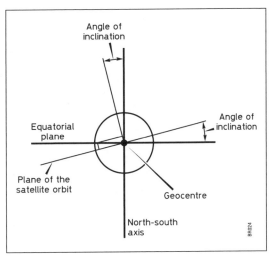

**Fig 10.2. Angle of inclination of a satellite orbit**

It is possible for a satellite to orbit the Earth in a number of different planes. The angle of inclination of a satellite orbit is shown in Fig 10.2. It is the angle between a line perpendicular to the plane of the orbit and a line passing through the poles. This means that an orbit directly above the equator will have an inclination of 0° (or 180°), and one passing over the poles will have an angle of 90°. Those orbits above the equator are generally called *equatorial orbits*, while those above the poles are called *polar orbits*.

The angle of elevation of a satellite is also of great importance because the ground station will only be able to maintain contact with the satellite while it is in view. If the angle it appears above the horizontal is too small then the line-of-sight path may be obstructed by a ground-based object. Some additional loss may also be incurred on the signal passage through the atmosphere in general and also the ionosphere, as low-angle paths will have a much greater path length passing through this area. In general it is accepted that an angle of 5° is the minimum for satisfactory operation.

In order to be able to use a satellite, the ground station must be able to receive its signal or be able to transmit one back to it. Normally this requires a directional antenna, and if the satellite is moving then the antenna must be able to adequately track its movement. In the case of geostationary satellites the antenna can remain fixed once it is directed towards them, but for all others a means of following them is required.

## Ground-to-satellite paths

As signals travel from the ground to the satellite they encounter four main regions, namely the troposphere, what is often termed *inner free space* (above the troposphere and below the ionosphere), the ionosphere, and the outer free space. Transmission in free space has unity refractive index and is lossless (apart from the spreading effect that reduces the signal power over a fixed area with distance away from the source but without any actual power loss).

The troposphere and ionosphere have refractive indices that differ from unity. The troposphere is greater than unity and the ionosphere is less than unity, and as a result refraction and absorption occur. In addition to this the ionosphere is a magneto-ionic region and this induces *Faraday rotation* onto the polarisation of the signal.

### Faraday rotation

The Faraday rotation of a signal causes different elements of a signal to travel in different ways, creating some problems with reception. A linearly polarised signal can be considered as two contra-rotating circularly polarised signals. The phase velocities of these two signals vary in a magnetic medium such as the ionosphere and as a result the polarisation of the signal changes. The degree of change is dependent upon the state of the ionosphere and it follows the same pattern as that experienced for HF ionospheric communications, changing over the course of the day, with the seasons and over the sunspot cycle.

### Ionospheric scintillations

This name is used to describe a number of variations of amplitude, phase, polarisation angle and angle of arrival that occur with signals. The variations occur in the short term (typically between one and 15 seconds) and they apply to signals well into the microwave region.

They are caused primarily by the variations in electron density arising in the E region, often as a result of sporadic E, but also in the F layer where a spreading effect is the cause. The level of scintillation is dependent upon a number of factors, including the location of the Earth station and the state of the ionosphere, as a result of the location, the sunspot cycle, the level of geomagnetic activity, latitude, and local time of day.

The scintillations are more intense in equatorial regions, falling with increasing latitude away from the equator but then rising at high latitudes in the auroral zone. The effects are also found to decrease with increasing frequency, and are therefore negligible when using frequencies above 1–2GHz.

### Tropospheric effects

There are a number of effects that the troposphere introduces, including signal bending, scintillation and attenuation.

The bending in the troposphere is in the opposite sense to that in the ionosphere because the refractive index is greater than unity, and it is also frequency independent. This gives the signals a greater range than would be expected as a result of the direct geometric line of sight. Tropospheric ducting and extended range effects that are experienced by terrestrial VHF and UHF communications may also be experienced when low angles of elevation are used.

Scintillations induced by the troposphere are often greater than those seen as a result of the ionosphere. They occur as a result of the turbulence in the atmosphere where areas of differing refractive index move around as a result of the wind or convection currents. The degree to which the scintillations occur is dependent upon the angle of inclination, and above angles of around 15° the effect can normally be ignored. At angles between 5 and 10° the changes can often be around 6dB at frequencies of around 5GHz.

## Doppler shift

With the fact that satellites, particularly those in low earth orbits, move very quickly, a Doppler frequency shift is apparent in many cases. With the satellite moving towards the Earth station the frequency appears higher than nominal, and then as it moves away the apparent frequency falls. The degree of shift is dependent upon a number of factors, including the speed of the satellite (more correctly its speed relative to the Earth station) and the frequencies in use. Shifts of the order of 10kHz may be experienced. As most satellites operate in a cross-mode configuration, the Doppler shift is not just applicable to the band on which the signal is received, but to the cumulative effect of the uplink and downlink transmissions. In many instances the effects will subtract because of the way the satellite mixing process is configured.

## Path lengths and path losses

The path length to satellites can introduce some significant losses as a result of distances involved. For LEO satellites this may not be significant but for those in geostationary orbits significant path lengths can be encountered. There is a minimum distance of 35,860km (22,300 miles) and this introduces a small but significant delay of 0.24 seconds for each of the uplink and downlink paths. This delay can make telephone conversations rather difficult when satellite links are used. It can also be seen when news reporters are using satellite links. When asked a question from the broadcaster's studio, the reporter appears to take some time to answer. This delay is the reason why many long-distance links use cables rather than satellites as the delays incurred are far less.

The loss due to the path length can be calculated from the formula:

$$\text{Loss (dB)} = 22 + 20 \log_{10} (R/\lambda)$$

where $R$ is the range and $\lambda$ is the wavelength in the same units as the range.

From this it can be seen that for a satellite in geostationary orbit the loss may be between 195 and 213dB for frequencies between 4 and 30GHz. The loss will normally be greater than this because this calculation assumes that the satellite is directly over the ground station and the path length is 35,860km.

## EME

Although satellites are a very effective means of communication as an active transponder above the Earth, it is also possible to use passive reflectors. In the early days of satellites the USA launched a large reflector satellite known as *Echo*. This provided a large surface that could be used to reflect radio signals, and of course it was clearly visible from the Earth.

It is also possible to use the Moon as a passive reflector in a form of communication known as *EME* (Earth-Moon-Earth) or *moonbounce*. In view

**Fig 10.3. The Moon. The surface is rough with many craters and features that mean any signal reflected from its surface has elements with varying phases. The overall reflection efficiency is around 6% (Image courtesy NASA/JPL-Caltech)**

of the very much greater distances and the fact that the Moon's surface is not an ideal reflector, the path losses are colossal but nevertheless it is still a form of communication that many radio amateurs regularly use.

The Moon is around 385,000km from the Earth. Its surface is also not a perfect reflector and only reflects about 6% of the power that reaches it. Added to the path loss for the signal travelling to and from the Moon, the overall path loss is around 251dB on 144MHz and 270dB on 1296MHz.

When using this form of communication very high powers, directive antennas and very sensitive receivers are required to overcome the losses. The distance of the Moon and its diameter of 3475km means it subtends an angle of only 0.52° to observers on the Earth. In order to illuminate it with little wasted power either side, highly directive antennas are required. Also these antennas must be completely steerable to be able to track its position.

Although frequencies as low as 50MHz have been used, it is more normal to use 144MHz, 432-MHz or 1296MHz where highly directive antennas with very high gains can be used to overcome the path losses.

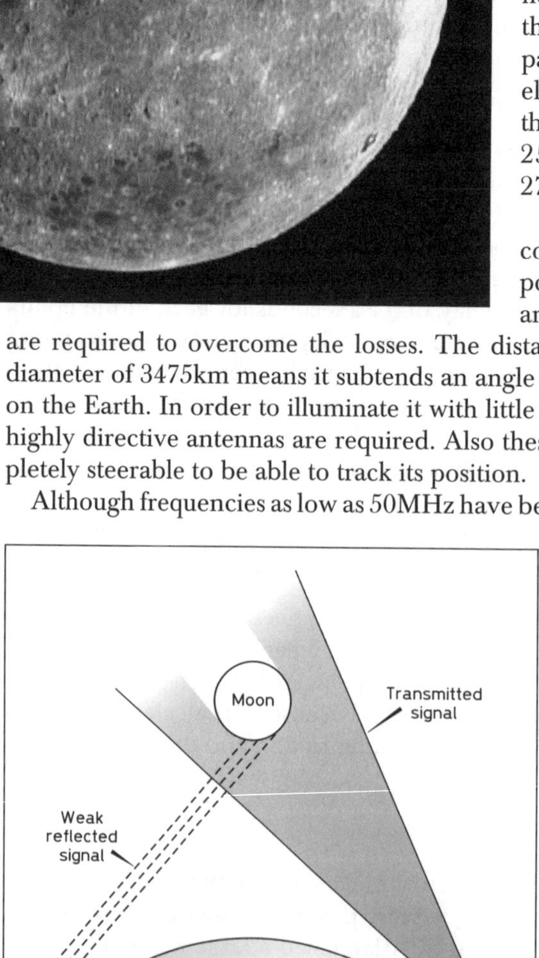

In addition to the path losses themselves the signals are subject to the same effects of Faraday rotation as encountered when communicating via satellite. At frequencies of 1296MHz and above it is not a problem, but on 432MHz it is believed that rotations

**Fig 10.4. EME communications**

up to 360° are common, and below this the signal may rotate through several complete revolutions. This may result in stations only being able to communicate in one direction at times.

An additional effect known as *libration fading* occurs because the surface of the Moon is not flat and the reflected signal consists of a variety of wavefronts, each with differing phases because the distance travelled by each one is slightly different due to the rough Moon surface. The received reflected signal is therefore a sum of all the wavefronts. As the Earth and the Moon are moving relative to each other the sum of these wavefronts is always changing and this results in a signal onto which is superimposed a rapid flutter as well as deep fading (sometimes up to 20dB) and some peaks. See Fig 10.5.

The relative movement of the Earth and the Moon can result in some degree of Doppler shift being added to the signals. This will vary according to the relative movements of the two bodies and also to the frequency in use.

Another problem can be that as stations are located at different positions around the Earth, a horizontally polarised signal in one area will be at right-angles to a horizontally polarised signal a quarter of the way round the globe. This spatial polarisation problem adds to the difficulties caused by Faraday rotation.

The use of EME propagation is a challenge but it can yield some excellent results. Those with the right equipment are able to make contacts with stations in many different areas of the globe when the Moon is in the right position relative to the Earth. In this way it is a challenging and interesting form of propagation to utilise.

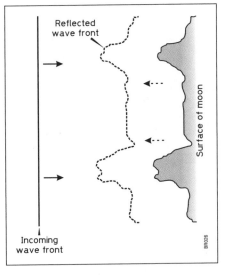

**Fig 10.5. After reflection by the Moon, wavefronts have a variety of phases which sum to give the overall signal. As these change with the relative movements of the Earth and the Moon this results in libration fading**

# Index

**A**

A index . . . . . . . . . . . . . . 75
Amateur bands . . . . . . . . 67
Angle diversity . . . . . . . . 82
Angle of incidence . . . . . . 41
Apogee . . . . . . . . . . . . . . 95
Ascending node . . . . . . . 94
Atmosphere . . . . . . . . . . 13
  layers . . . . . . . . . . . . . . 14
Attenuation
  ionospheric . . . . . . . . . 38
  tropospheric . . . . . . . . 82
Auroras . . . . . . . . . . . . . . 62

**B**

Backscatter . . . . . . . . . . . 64
Bands
  HF . . . . . . . . . . . . . . . . 67
  VHF and above . . . . . . 80
Beacons . . . . . . . . . . . . . . 72
Bending, signal . . . . . . . . 96
Blackouts . . . . . . . . . . . . 61

**C**

Charges, electric . . . . . . . . 1
Chordal hop . . . . . . . . . . 48
Chromosphere, solar . . . 26
Circular orbit . . . . . . . . . 94
Circular polarisation . . . . 5
CME . . . . . . . . . . . . 33, 60
Conditions
  assessing tropospheric . 80
  enhanced tropospheric . 78
  monitoring ionospheric 72
Convection zone . . . . . . . 25
Conversion, frequency to
    wavelength . . . . . . . . . 4
Corkscrew rule . . . . . . . . . 2
Corona, solar . . . . . . . . . 26
Coronagraph . . . . . . . . . 33
Coronal holes . . . . . . . . . 34

Coronal mass ejection
  (CME) . . . . . . . 33, 60
Critical frequency . . . . . 43
Cross-polarisation . . . . . . 5
Cycles per second . . . . . . 3

**D**

D region . . . . . . . . . . . 18, 38
Dead zone . . . . . . . . . . . 43
Dellinger effect . . . . . . . . 62
Descending node . . . . . . 94
Diffraction . . . . . . . . . . . . 7
Distances, meteor scatter . 89
Doppler shift   8, 90, 97, 99
Duct, tropospheric . . . . . 78
Dynamic equilibrium . . . . 17

**E**

E region . . . . . . . . . . 18, 39
Electromagnetic wave . . . . 1
Elliptical orbit . . . . . . . . 94
Elliptical polarisation . . . . 5
EME . . . . . . . . . . . . . . . . 97
Enhanced tropospheric
    conditions . . . . . . . . 78
Enhancement, pre-auroral 64
Equatorial orbits . . . . . . . 95
Extraordinary wave . . . . . 43

**F**

F region . . . . . . . . . . . . . 19
F1 region . . . . . . . . . . . . 40
F2 region . . . . . . . . . . . . 40
Fading . . . . . . . . . . . . . . . 46
  libration . . . . . . . . . . . 99
  selective . . . . . . . . . . . 47
  tropospheric . . . . . . . . 80
Faraday rotation . . . . . . . 96
Field intensity . . . . . . . . . . 2
Field strength . . . . . . . .3, 9
Flares, solar . . . . . . . . . . 32
Flux, solar . . . . . . . . . 31, 74

FOT . . . . . . . . . . . . . . . . 46
Free electrons . . . . . . . . . 15
Free space propagation  8, 12
Fréquence optimum de
    travail (FOT) . . . . . . 46
Frequency . . . . . . . . . . . . . 3
  critical . . . . . . . . . . . . . 43
  dependence of
    propagation . . . . . . . 40
  diversity . . . . . . . . . . . 82
  lowest usable (LUF) . . . 45
  maximum usable (MUF) 44
  meteor scatter . . . . . . . 89
  optimum working
    (OWF) . . . . . . . . . . 45

**G**

Gases, atmospheric . . . . . 14
Geocentre . . . . . . . . . . . . 94
Geomagnetic storm . . . . . 60
Geostationary orbit . . . . . 94
Granules, solar . . . . . . . . 26
Grey-line propagation . . . 53
Ground track . . . . . . . . . 94
Ground-wave
    propagation . . . . 12, 35

**H**

Hertz . . . . . . . . . . . . . . . . . 3
Huygen's principle . . . . . . 7

**I**

Indicators, solar and
    geomagnetic . . . . . . 74
Interface zone, solar . . . . 25
Ionisation . . . . . . . . . . . . 15
  geographical variations  20
Ionogram . . . . . . . . . 44, 73
Ionosondes . . . . . . . . . . . 73
Ionosphere . . . . . . . . . . . 15
  indicators . . . . . . . . . . 31
  layers . . . . . . . . . . . . . . 37

propagation . . . . . . . . 12
regions . . . . . . . . . . . . 17
scintillations . . . . . . . . 96
storms . . . . . . . . . . . . 60
variations . . . . . . . . . . 19
Ions . . . . . . . . . . . . . . . . 16

**K**

K index . . . . . . . . . . . . . . 75

**L**

Layers
atmospheric . . . . . . . . . 14
ionospheric . . . . . . . . . 37
solar interior . . . . . . . . 23
LEO . . . . . . . . . . . . . . . . 94
Libration fading . . . . . . . . 99
Linear polarisation . . . . . . . 5
Losses, path . 10, 46, 48, 97
Low earth orbit (LEO) . . . 94
Lowest usable frequency
(LUF) . . . . . . . . . . . . 45
Lyman α radiation . . . . . . 18

**M**

Magnetic fields . . . . . . . . . . 2
Earth's . . . . . . . . . . . . . . 20
Sun's . . . . . . . . . . . . . . 25
Magnetosheath . . . . . . . . . 21
Magnetosphere . . . . . . . . . 21
Maximum usable frequency
(MUF) . . . . . . . . . . . . 44
Mesosphere . . . . . . . . . . . 14
Meteors . . . . . . . . . . . . . . 85
Meteor scatter . . . . . . . . . 85
Meteor showers . . . . . . . . 86
Meteor trails . . . . . . . . . . 88
Mirages . . . . . . . . . . . . . . . 7
Modes of propagation . . . 12
Moonbounce . . . . . . . . . . 97
MUF . . . . . . . . . . . . . . . . 44
Multi-path propagation . . 11
Multiple reflections . . . . . 47

**N**

N units . . . . . . . . . . . . . . 78
Near-vertical-incidence sky
wave (NVIS) . . . . . . . 56
North pole, magnet . . . . . . 2
Northern Lights . . . . . . . . 62
NVIS . . . . . . . . . . . . . . . . 56

**O**

O wave . . . . . . . . . . . . . . 43
Occulting disk . . . . . . . . . 33
Operating techniques, meteor
scatter . . . . . . . . . . . 90
Operational MUF . . . . . . 44
Optimum working frequency
(OWF) . . . . . . . . . . . 45
Orbits, satellites . . . . . . . . 93
Ordinary wave . . . . . . . . 43

Over-dense meteor trail . . 88
OWF . . . . . . . . . . . . . . . . 45

**P**

Path losses . . 10, 46, 48, 97
Paths
ionospheric
nomenclature . . . . . . 49
meteor scatter . . . . . . . 89
multi- . . . . . . . . . . . . . 11
signal . . . . . . . . . . . . . 49
PCA . . . . . . . . . . . . . . . . 61
Penumbra, sunspot . . . . . 28
Perigee . . . . . . . . . . . . . . 95
Photosphere . . . . . . . . . . 25
Planetary K index . . . . . . 75
Polar cap absorption
(PCA) . . . . . . . . . . . 61
Polar diagram . . . . . . . . . 42
Polar orbits . . . . . . . . . . . 95
Polarisation . . . . . . . . . . . . 5
Pores . . . . . . . . . . . . . . . 28
Posigrade orbit . . . . . . . . 94
Potential, electrostatic . . . . 1
Potential gradient . . . . . . . 2
Pre-auroral enhancement . 64
Predictions of propagation
conditions . . . . . . . . 76

**R**

Radiant, meteor shower . . 86
Radiation, solar 4, 15, 31, 60
Lyman α . . . . . . . . . . 18
Radiative zone, solar . . . . 25
Radio waves . . . . . . . . . . . 3
Reflection . . . . . . . . . . . . . 6
multiple . . . . . . . . . . . 47
Refraction . . . . . . . . . . 7, 77
Retrograde orbit . . . . . . . 94
Rotation, solar . . . . . . . . 27

**S**

Satellites . . . . . . . . . . . . 93
Scatter volume . . . . . . . . 82
Scintillations, ionospheric 96
Seasonal changes . . . . . . 19
Selective fading . . . . . . . . 47
SFU . . . . . . . . . . . . . . . . 74
Short-wave fades (SWF) . . 62
SID . . . . . . . . . . . . . . . . 61
Skip distance . . . . . . . . . 42
Skip zone . . . . . . . . . . . . 43
Sky waves . . . . . . . . . . . 37
Snell's law . . . . . . . . . . . . 7
Solar disturbances . . . . . . 31
Solar flux . . . . . . . . . 31, 74
units (SFU) . . . . . . . . 74
Solar radiation storms . . . 61
Solar wind . . . . . . . . 21, 31
South pole, magnet . . . . . . 2
Southern Lights . . . . . . . . 62
Spectrum, electromagnetic 4

Sporadic E . . . . . . . . . . . 49
Sporadic meteors . . . . 86, 87
Spread F . . . . . . . . . . . . . 53
Storms, ionospheric . . . . . 60
Stratosphere . . . . . . . . . . 14
Sudden ionospheric
disturbance (SID) . . 61
Sun . . . . . . . . . . . . . . . . 23
chromosphere . . . . . . . 26
convection zone . . . . . . 25
core . . . . . . . . . . . . . . 24
corona . . . . . . . . . . . . 26
disturbances . . . . . . . . 31
flares . . . . . . . . . . . . . 32
flux . . . . . . . . . . . . . . 74
granules . . . . . . . . . . . 26
interface zone . . . . . . . 25
interior . . . . . . . . . . . . 23
photosphere . . . . . . . . 25
radiation storms . . . . . . 61
radiative zone . . . . . . . 25
rotation . . . . . . . . . . . . 27
solar wind . . . . . . . 21, 31
supergranules . . . . . . . 26
tachocline . . . . . . . . . . 25
Sunspots . . . . . . . . . . . . 28
cycle . . . . . . . . . . . . . 30
numbers . . . . . . . . . . . 29
Sunspot Index Data
Centre . . . . . . . . . . . 30
Supergranules, solar . . . . . 26
Surface wave . . . . . . . . . 35
SWF . . . . . . . . . . . . . . . . 62

**T**

Tachocline . . . . . . . . . . . 25
Temperature inversion . . . 79
Terminator . . . . . . . . . . . 54
Thermosphere . . . . . . . . 14
Top Band . . . . . . . . . . . . 68
Tropopause . . . . . . . . . . . 15
Troposcatter . . . . . . . . . . 82
Troposphere . . . . . . . 14, 15
duct . . . . . . . . . . . . . . 78
propagation . . . . . . 12, 77

**U**

Umbra, sunspot . . . . . . . . 28
Under-dense meteor trail . 88

**V**

Van Allen belts . . . . . . . . 21
Velocity, waves . . . . . . . . . 4
Vertical incidence sounders
(VIS) . . . . . . . . . . . 73
Virtual height . . . . . . . . . 44

**W**

Wave, electromagnetic . . . . 1
Wavelength . . . . . . . . . . . . 3
Waves, radio . . . . . . . . . . . 3
Wolf, Rudolf . . . . . . . . . . 29

Adrio Communications is a provider of value-for-money technical services for electronics engineering support, training, and technical journalism.

With many years of experience in the electronics industry and a successful track record from electronics design to technical management as well as in the marketing arena and technical journalism, we are able to meet a variety of the needs for your company.

Call or email us today to find out exactly how we can help your business succeed. Alternatively check out the website for further information.

Contact:

    Ian Poole
    Adrio Communications
    5 Meadway
    Staines
    TW18 2PW
    United Kingdom

    Tel: +44 (0) 1784 455511
    Email: ian.poole@adrio-communications.com

**www.adrio-communications.com**

*Technical journalism, training, electronic engineering*

# Other Titles By Ian Poole

### HF Amateur Radio

The HF or short wave bands are one of the most interesting areas of amateur radio. Stations from all around the globe can be heard and many interesting contacts can be made. Operating on these frequencies requires many skills if the most is to be made of the time that is available.

HF Amateur Radio deals with the radio spectrum from 1.8 to 30MHz. This book takes the reader through setting up an efficient amateur radio station, which equipment to choose, installation, and the best antenna for your location. It is packed full of information including which frequencies to use, how to operate on the bands, and the advantages of each type of transmission. HF Amateur Radio will benefit those new to amateur radio, anyone contemplating exploring the world below 30MHz, and just about any licensed amateur or short-wave listener who feels he could get more out of his station.

**£13.99 Plus p&p**

### Guide to VHF/UHF Amateur Radio

The VHF and UHF band are some of the most interesting, useful and challenging of those available. Ian Poole explains just how to get the most from your VHF/UHF station: by studying the weather to predict greatly enhanced propagation; by using the correct part of each band; by choosing the right transmitter, receiver and antenna, and by using the correct procedure. A chapter explains how to transmit and receive computer data on these bands.

This hand-sized book contains everything you will need to help you enjoy VHF/UHF amateur radio to the full.

**£8.99 Plus p&p**

### Amateur Radio Explained

Have you ever needed to explain to someone what amateur radio is all about? Have you ever wanted something to help fan the flames of someone's initial interest in the hobby? Do you give talks about amateur radio? If so, this book will help you. Building on the success of Amateur Radio for Beginners (thousands of copies sold), this new volume covers setting up a station, what you are likely to hear on each band, how to receive and transmit, what's involved in getting a licence, codes, propagation, equipment, construction and much more. In short an ideal introduction to the diverse world of amateur radio.

**£9.99 Plus p&p**

All Prices are subject to change without notice E&OE